Table of Contents

S0-AHC-227

Teacher's Annotated Pages

Name _____

LANGUAGE AND USAGE

1 | What Is a Sentence?

> **Sentences:** Band music is very popular with people of all ages.
> People have listened to bands for hundreds of years.
> **Sentence Fragments:** Band music.
> Is very popular with people of all ages.
> For hundreds of years.

A. Write *S* after each group of words that is a sentence. Write *F* after each group of words that is a sentence fragment.

1. John Philip Sousa was a famous bandleader. _____

   From 1854 to 1932. _____

2. Sousa was born in Washington, D.C. _____

   Visited many places around the world. _____

3. More than one hundred marches. _____

   Sousa wrote music. _____

4. You probably know some of his music. _____

   ''The Stars and Stripes Forever.'' _____

5. Can listen to his records in school. _____

   You can buy records of Sousa's marches. _____

B. Change each fragment above into a complete sentence.

6. _____

7. _____

8. _____

9. _____

10. _____

(continued)

Level 5 Unit 1 The Sentence   *(Use with pupil book pages 14–15.)*
Skill: Students will identify complete sentences and will correct sentence fragments.

LANGUAGE AND USAGE

1 | **What Is a Sentence?**   *(continued from page 1)*

C. Writing Application: A Music Review

Think about a record that you like. Write five sentences telling why you like it. Make sure that your sentences are complete.

★ Enrichment ★

Find the five complete sentences below. Write the sentences in order on the lines. Then circle the first letter of each sentence. The letters you circle will spell the name of something that is important in a band.

1. Several kinds of bands.
2. Dance bands are popular.
3. On records or on tape.
4. Radios play band music.
5. Usually people like bands.
6. Once in a while a loud noise.
7. Playing in a band.
8. Many students like Sousa's music.
9. Trying to play like John Philip Sousa.
10. Sousa wrote a book about his life.

_____

_____

_____

_____

_____

LANGUAGE AND USAGE

2 | Four Kinds of Sentences

> Declarative Sentence: There are many ways of sending messages.
> Interrogative Sentence: How many ways do you know?
> Imperative Sentence: Take this note to your mother.
> Exclamatory Sentence: What a strange message this is!

A. Write the correct end punctuation for each sentence. Then label each sentence *declarative, interrogative, imperative,* or *exclamatory.*

  1. Have you ever received a telegram ____   _____

  2. How exciting it is ____   _____

  3. Telegrams were popular before we had telephones ____   _____

  4. Do you know who invented the telegraph ____   _____

  5. Read about it here ____   _____

  6. Samuel F. B. Morse was one of the inventors ____   _____

  7. What a clever person he was ____   _____

  8. He also invented Morse code ____   _____

  9. Do you know how to use Morse code ____   _____

 10. Learn to use Morse code ____   _____

 11. Have you heard that Morse was also an artist ____   _____

 12. What wonderful portraits he painted ____   _____

 13. Have you seen any of his paintings ____   _____

 14. Some of his work is displayed in New York ____   _____

 15. Please try to find out more about Morse ____   _____

 16. Look up his name in the encyclopedia ____   _____

 17. What interesting facts you will discover ____   _____

(continued)

LANGUAGE AND USAGE

2 | Four Kinds of Sentences *(continued from page 3)*

B. Writing Application: A Message

You have been shipwrecked on an island in the middle of the ocean. You find a piece of paper, a pencil, and a bottle. Write a message to put into the bottle. Your message must include one declarative sentence, one interrogative sentence, one imperative sentence, and one exclamatory sentence.

Enrichment

The students in Mr. Novak's class wanted to make the invitations to their party sound like telegrams. Instead of using end punctuation, they ended every sentence with the word *STOP.* Rewrite the invitation on the lines below. Replace each *STOP* with the correct end punctuation.

TELEGRAM

We are having a party Thursday afternoon STOP Can you
come STOP It will be such fun STOP Bring this invitation
with you STOP Present it at the door STOP

                                    Mr. Novak's class

TELEGRAM

_____

_____

_____

Now underline the first word in each imperative sentence you have written. The words form a hidden message. Write the message here.

_____

LANGUAGE AND USAGE

6 | Subjects in Imperative Sentences

> **Declarative Sentence: Joshua** mashed the potatoes.
> **Imperative Sentence: (You)** Mash the potatoes, please.

A. For each sentence, write *D* for declarative or *I* for imperative. Then write the simple subject of the sentence.

1. Potatoes are an ancient crop. ____ _____

2. Tell me more about potatoes. ____ _____

3. We eat the underground stem. ____ _____

4. Please give me some more facts. ____ _____

5. The vegetables first grew in South America. ____ _____

6. Spanish explorers took them to Europe. ____ _____

7. Please explain how they were grown. ____ _____

8. Inca Indians grew them in the mountains. ____ _____

9. They used potatoes to make a special flour. ____ _____

10. Guess how the flour was made. ____ _____

11. Let me think, please. ____ _____

12. Show me how it was done. ____ _____

13. The Incas mashed the potatoes with their feet. ____ _____

14. Imagine walking on all those potatoes. ____ _____

15. People still make potato flour today. ____ _____

16. Please don't ask me to do the mashing. ____ _____

B. Writing Application: Directions

Imagine that you have invented a new way of cooking potatoes. Write five or more sentences explaining your method. Include three imperative sentences. List the simple subject for each sentence you write.

(continued)

Enrichment

Complete this television advertisement for Tater potatoes. Write an imperative sentence under each television screen to show what each announcer is saying.

1.

_____

_____

3.

_____

_____

2.

_____

_____

4.

_____

_____

Now make up your own advertisement for a new kind of food. Draw your advertisement on another piece of paper.

Level 5 Unit 1 The Sentence *(Use with pupil book pages 24–25.)*
Skill: Students will write imperative sentences.

LANGUAGE AND USAGE

7 | Conjunctions

> Scientists **and** other people use thermometers.
> Thermometers can indicate a fever, **but** they cannot cure it.
> They can measure warm weather **or** indicate cold weather.

A. Complete each sentence. Write the conjunction that has the meaning given in parentheses.

1. The Fahrenheit _____ the Celsius are scales. **(joins together)**

2. Many people in the United States use Fahrenheit thermometers, _____ in Canada the Celsius scale is used. **(shows contrast)**

3. Do you use a Fahrenheit thermometer, _____ do you prefer a Celsius thermometer? **(shows choice)**

4. The two thermometers measure the same things _____ do this in different ways. **(shows contrast)**

5. On the Fahrenheit scale, water freezes at 32 degrees, _____ on the Celsius scale, it freezes at 0 degrees. **(shows contrast)**

6. The temperature of boiling water is 212 degrees Fahrenheit, _____ it is 100 degrees Celsius. **(shows contrast)**

7. Announcers _____ forecasters use either scale. **(joins together)**

8. They say ''Fahrenheit,'' _____ they say ''Celsius'' to let you know which one they are using. **(shows choice)**

9. Some announcers use _____ report both scales. **(joins together)**

10. Listen to the weather report tomorrow morning _____ find out which thermometer the announcer is using. **(joins together)**

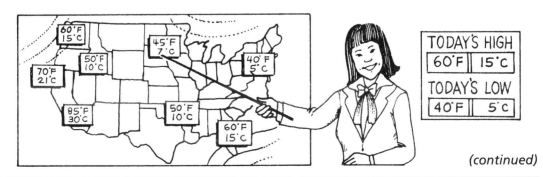

(continued)

Level 5 Unit 1 The Sentence *(Use with pupil book pages 26–27.)*
Skill: Students will use conjunctions in sentences.

7 | **Conjunctions** (continued from page 13)

B. Writing Application: Sentences

Congratulations! You are going to be on television tonight. You will give the weather report. Write five sentences, telling what the weather will be like tomorrow. Use a conjunction in each sentence.

Enrichment

The students in Mrs. Pizarro's class made up a game for conjunctions. In their game, *or* is worth 3 points, *but* is worth 2 points, and *and* is worth 1 point. Play the game by completing the following sentences with conjunctions. Write your points on the lines. WARNING: The conjunction must make sense in the sentence!

1. Galileo made a thermometer, _____ it was not accurate.

2. The device had a scale _____ was called a thermoscope.

3. The thermometer used water _____ other liquids.

4. The device didn't use alcohol, _____ others did.

5. Did Fahrenheit _____ Celsius first use mercury?

6. The first scales used boiling water, _____ they used melting ice as a fixed temperature.

7. New thermometers use air _____ work by electricity.

Add up your score. How many points did you get?

Stump a friend! On a separate sheet of paper, write five sentences in which more than one conjunction can make sense. Leave a blank line for each conjunction. See how many points your friend can get.

LANGUAGE AND USAGE

8 | Combining Sentences: Compound Subjects

Simple Subjects:	**Elsa** will mix colors.
	Eddie will mix colors.
Compound Subject:	**Elsa** <u>and</u> **Eddie** will mix colors.

A. Underline each conjunction. Write the simple subjects in each compound subject.

1. Elsa and Luis were learning about colors. _____

2. A rainbow or a prism can show you many colors.

   _____

3. Red, blue, and other colors make up a rainbow.

   _____

4. Red and yellow are primary colors. _____

5. Blue, yellow, and red can be combined to make other colors.

   _____

B. Combine each group of sentences into one sentence with a compound subject. Use the conjunction shown in parentheses.

6. Elsa read about color vision.   **(and)**
   Another student read about color vision.

   _____

7. Heredity can be the cause of color blindness.   **(or)**
   Disease can be the cause of color blindness.

   _____

8. Researchers have observed color vision in animals.   **(and)**
   Pet owners have observed color vision in animals.

   _____

9. Monkeys have color vision like humans.   **(and)**
   Many birds have color vision like humans.
   Some fish have color vision like humans.

   _____

(continued)

LANGUAGE AND USAGE

8 | **Combining Sentences: Compound Subjects** *(continued from page 15)*

C. Writing Application: A Newspaper Article

You are a reporter in the mighty kingdom of Mook. You have just been to a ball at the royal palace. Now you must write an article for the *Mook Daily Journal*. Write at least five sentences, describing the king's and queen's clothes. Be sure to mention the colors. Include three or more sentences with compound subjects.

★— Enrichment —★

Tell about your dream house by completing the compound subjects below.

1. _____ , _____ , and _____ live in my dream house.

2. _____ or _____ is the building material.

3. _____ , _____ , and _____ are the outside colors.

4. _____ or _____ is the color of the inside.

5. _____ or _____ is the color of my bedroom.

6. _____ , _____ , and _____ are in the yard.

7. _____ and _____ are secret places.

8. _____ or _____ is the location of the house.

9. _____ and _____ are in my room.

10. _____ and _____ are my favorite rooms.

Now draw the plan for your dream house on a separate piece of paper.

LANGUAGE AND USAGE

9 | Combining Sentences: Compound Predicates

Simple Predicates:	Phil **reads** many kinds of books.
	Phil **enjoys** many kinds of books.
Compound Predicate:	Phil **reads** and **enjoys** many kinds of books.

A. Underline each conjunction. Write the simple predicates in each compound predicate.

1. L. M. Montgomery's stories interest and amuse many readers. _____

2. She started as a teacher, married, and then became a writer.

   _____

3. An editor saw Montgomery's work or knew her reputation. _____

4. The editor met Montgomery, spoke to her, and asked her for a story.

   _____

5. She remembered and wrote about her days on Prince Edward Island.

   _____

6. She added more adventures and created *Anne of Green Gables*.

   _____

B. Combine each group of sentences into one sentence with a compound predicate. Use the conjunction in parentheses.

7. L. M. Montgomery wrote many other books.   **(and)**
   L. M. Montgomery published many other books.

   _____

8. Many people buy Montgomery's books.   **(or)**
   Many people borrow them from their friends.
   Many people take them out of the library.

   _____   _____

   _____

(continued)

LANGUAGE AND USAGE

9 | **Combining Sentences: Compound Predicates**   *(continued from page 17)*

C. Writing Application: A Book Review

Write five sentences about a book you have read. Tell something about the story and where it takes place. Explain why you did or did not like the book. Include three or more sentences with compound predicates in your review.

Enrichment

The travel guide below is all mixed-up. One simple predicate in each sentence is correct, but the other should be in a different sentence. Each incorrect predicate is underlined. Find the correct predicate in another sentence. Write the sentence correctly.

1. Prince Edward Island <u>flies</u> off Canada's coast and is its smallest province.

   _____

2. Many people <u>swim</u> or live on Prince Edward Island.

   _____

3. Some people <u>sightsee</u> or farm for a living.

   _____

4. Some farmers <u>attract</u> and sell potatoes.

   _____

5. Sandy white beaches line the shore and <u>grow</u> tourists.

   _____

6. Some tourists <u>visit</u>, ski, or sail in the water.

   _____

7. Other tourists <u>fish</u> and shop in the towns.

   _____

8. A tourist takes a boat or <u>lies</u> to Prince Edward Island.

   _____

LANGUAGE AND USAGE

10 | Combining Sentences: Compound Sentences

Simple Sentences:	Fish can live in an aquarium.
	Water plants can live there too.
Compound Sentence:	Fish can live in an aquarium, <u>and</u> water plants can live there too.

A. Combine each pair of sentences into a compound sentence. Use the conjunction that has the meaning given in parentheses. Use commas correctly.

1. Chen loves aquariums. He has never been to one. **(shows contrast)**

   _____

2. The town has no aquarium. Chen has read about one. **(shows contrast)**

   _____

   _____

3. He reads about the history. He discovers new facts. **(joins together)**

   _____

4. Ancient Egyptians had aquariums. The Romans did too. **(joins together)**

   _____

   _____

5. They were popular in China. Japan also had them. **(shows contrast)**

   _____

6. Chen may visit an aquarium. He may make his own. **(shows choice)**

   _____

7. He could make an aquarium. He could buy one. **(shows choice)**

   _____

8. Chen plans his aquarium. He chooses his fish. **(joins together)**

   _____

(continued)

LANGUAGE AND USAGE

10 | Combining Sentences: Compound Sentences (continued from page 19)

B. Writing Application: A Description

You have two fish named Floppy and Flippy. Although their names are alike, the fish are very different. Write five sentences, describing the fish and telling what they do. At least three of the sentences should be compound sentences.

Enrichment

The poem below is about a very strange island. Complete the compound sentences to tell just how odd the island is. Make the last word of each sentence you write rhyme with the last word in the line above it.

The Island of Why

Curtis lives on the island of Why.

There all birds can swim _____

On the island of Why is a very strange town.

The ground is up _____

Why is odd, or so I've been told.

Grandparents are young _____

The island of Why must be quite a sight.

It's dark in the daytime _____

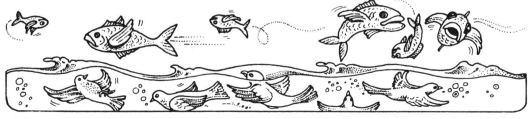

Level 5 Unit 1 The Sentence   *(Use with pupil book pages 32–33.)*
Skill: Students will write compound sentences.

LANGUAGE AND USAGE

 Run-on Sentences

> **Run-on Sentence:** Helen lives in Arizona Tanya lives in Alaska.
> **Correct:** Helen lives in Arizona. **T**anya lives in Alaska.
> **Also Correct:** Helen lives in Arizona, but Tanya lives in Alaska.

A. Correct these run-on sentences. First, separate each one into two sentences. Then write each one as a compound sentence.

1. People dress one way for the cold they dress another way for the heat.

   Separate: _____

   _____

   Compound: _____

   _____

2. Some clothes keep you warm some keep you cool.

   Separate: _____

   Compound: _____

3. Wool is warm cotton is cool.

   Separate: _____

   Compound: _____

4. Heat escapes from your head a hat can keep you warm.

   Separate: _____

   Compound: _____

5. White clothes reflect the sun they keep you cool.

   Separate: _____

   Compound: _____

(continued)

LANGUAGE AND USAGE

11 | **Run-on Sentences**   *(continued from page 21)*

B. Writing Application: A Letter

You have just moved to the North Pole. Write a letter to your friend in Florida.
Tell your friend about your life. Be sure you do not write any run-on sentences.

 Enrichment

This radio announcer was so excited about a new product that she ran all of her
sentences together! Help her by rewriting the advertisement. Correct each run-
on sentence.

> Thermesh is a new space-age material it is made of special metallic fibers no
> other fiber is like thermesh it will keep you warm in the winter it will keep you cool
> in the summer it never needs ironing it won't crush, tear, or rust thermesh is water-
> proof use it as a tent it is soft enough for a baby's blanket you will never find an-
> other fabric like thermesh why should you settle for less this miracle material is
> not sold in stores supplies are limited don't miss your chance order thermesh today!

_____

_____

_____

_____

_____

_____

_____

_____

Level 5 Unit 1 The Sentence   *(Use with pupil book pages 34–35.)*
Skill: Students will correct run-on sentences.

COMPOSITION SKILL: PERSONAL NARRATIVE

Writing a Good Beginning

> **Poor Beginning:** Last week was my grandmother's birthday. We had a party.
> **Better Beginning:** Have you ever tried to blow out sixty candles at once?

A. Write two good beginnings for each of the stories below. Put a check next to the one you like better.

1. . . . The lights had never before gone out when I was home alone. I felt my way along the walls, found the light switch, and flicked it up and down. Nothing happened. "Now what?" I asked myself.

   Beginning: _____

   _____

   Beginning: _____

   _____

2. . . . The line for the roller coaster was getting shorter. My turn would be coming any minute. I was nervous about my first ride. Would I be scared? Excited? Sick? I swallowed hard.

   Beginning: _____

   _____

   Beginning: _____

   _____

B. Think of a funny, sad, or frightening experience that you have had or have observed. Write two good beginnings for a story about what happened. Put a check next to the better beginning.

Beginning: _____

_____

Beginning: _____

_____

Supplying Details

> **Poor Detail:** I was nervous.
> **Interesting Detail:** My palms were sweating and my knees were shaking as I walked to the front of the room.

Read the following paragraphs. Then rewrite each paragraph, adding details to make each one more interesting.

A.   The wind was howling. I looked out the window at the street. It was empty. I saw a trash can blow over and roll down the street. A branch of a tree broke. It fell onto the roof next door.

_____

_____

_____

_____

_____

_____

_____

B.   It was my first day at a new school. I was so scared that I walked into the wrong classroom at first. Finally I found my room. Everyone looked at me. The teacher moved toward me and said hello. Then I tripped.

_____

_____

_____

_____

_____

_____

Writing Dialogue

> "Use quotation marks whenever you write dialogue," said Mrs. Garcia. Chris added, "Begin a new paragraph for each change of speaker too."

A. Rewrite the sentences below as a dialogue. Put quotation marks around the exact words that each person might say. Try to make the dialogue sound the way people really talk.

Ari said that he had an idea. I asked him what it was. He said that we should go swimming. I agreed.

_____

_____

_____

_____

B. Look at the illustration below. Write a dialogue between the two characters. Write at least two sentences for each character.

_____

_____

_____

_____

_____

_____

COMPOSITION SKILL: PERSONAL NARRATIVE

Writing a Good Title

> **Poor Title:** My Sister's Pet Hamster Sleepy
> **Good Title:** Why I Hate Hamsters

Read each story below. Write two good titles for each one. Underline the title that you like better in each pair.

A. _____

_____

    I felt as if I had been waiting for hours. I began to worry. Maybe no one would come to meet me after all. At least I wasn't alone. The bus station was crowded with travelers. As I waited, I tried to imagine where they had come from or where they were going. I was daydreaming so much that I hardly noticed the familiar face in the crowd.

B. _____

_____

    One of my favorite things about living in New Mexico is visiting Carlsbad Caverns. A guide shows visitors huge underground rocks that look like giant icicles. They are called stalactites and stalagmites. There are very few living things in the caves. However, there is one cave called the Bat Cave. It is my favorite.

C. _____

_____

    I went snorkeling with my sister. The instructor gave us each a mask with a breathing tube. We saw crabs, clam shells, and beautifully colored fish. Being underwater felt mysterious. I can't wait to go again!

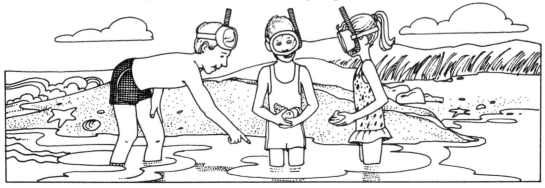

THE WRITING PROCESS: PERSONAL NARRATIVE

Step 3: Revise

Have I	yes
changed the beginning so that it will catch a reader's attention?	☐
added details that give a clear picture?	☐
added dialogue that brings the characters to life?	☐
written an interesting title that does not tell too much?	☐

Revise the following story. Use the check list above to help you. Check off each box when you have finished your revision.

● Use the space above each line, on the sides, and below the paragraph for your changes.

Going Sailing for the First Time

My dad asked me if I wanted to go sailing. He said it was a

perfect day. The wind was just right for sailing. I told Dad I

would like to go. Dad's boat is really pretty. If you saw it, you

would know that it was designed to go fast. Dad pushed us away

from the dock. I hoisted the mainsail, and it filled with wind.

The boat sailed across the water, making little waves. Dad said

to pull a little tighter on the sheet. That's the rope attached to

the sail. I did, and the boat leaned to one side. I told Dad that I

was scared, but he explained that we were just heeling. The boat

moved very fast. It was very exciting!

Step 4: Proofread

the hole was ~~dep~~, *deep* and the ~~diggers~~ *diggers* were tired.

A. Proofread the following story. Find three mistakes in spelling, one mistake in capitalization, one missing end mark, one run-on sentence, and one mistake in a compound sentence. Use proofreading marks to correct the mistakes. Use a dictionary to check your spelling.

"How many pennies are in the jar?" Mr. Phipp asked when we came into his store. I took a carefull look at the jar It was big and the pennies were piled to the top. I took a wild guess there are six letturs in my name. Mr. Phipp's store is at 102 Main Street. I multiplied 102 by 6. that came to 612, the exact nuber of pennies in the jar!

B. Proofread this story. There are four mistakes in spelling, one mistake in end punctuation, and one mistake in a compound sentence. Correct the mistakes.

In the night I had an idea for a story. I didn't want to loose it. I grabbed some papr. It was on my desk. I wrote some notes and got back into bed. The story idea was great and I was exited about it! The next morning I couldn't find my notes? The story idea and my notes had all been a drem!

LANGUAGE AND USAGE

 What Is a Noun?

Persons:	relative	Sara	Uncle Ed
Places:	bay	Hudson Bay	Bay of Fundy
Things:	games	Olympics	baseball
Ideas:	safety	problem	agreement

A. Write the nouns in each sentence.

1. My aunt works at Woods Hole as a scientist.

   _____

2. Aunt Jane has an understanding of the habits of whales.

   _____

3. These mammals spend their entire life in the sea.

   _____

4. These animals are the largest creatures on earth.

   _____

5. Their brains may be as big as watermelons.

   _____

6. Biologists are studying ways to measure their intelligence.

   _____

7. Some species that have neared extinction are now protected.

   _____

8. New laws in the United States call for their protection.

   _____

B. Writing Application: A Paragraph

   Imagine that you have suddenly become as big as a whale! Write a paragraph, telling about things you can and cannot do because of your size. Circle each noun in your paragraph.

(continued)

LANGUAGE AND USAGE

1 | **What Is a Noun?**   *(continued from page 29)*

(continued from page 29)

★ Enrichment ★

Below is a map of Blue Bay. Here are some symbols used on the map:

 lighthouse   dock   whale

lifeguard   water ～～   ship

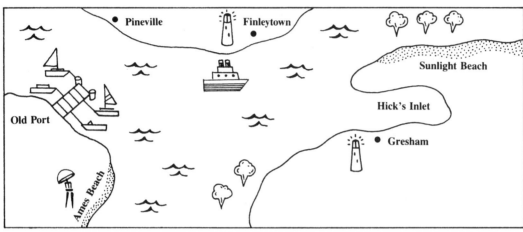

Use the map to find the answers to the questions. Write a complete sentence for each answer. Underline the nouns in your sentences.

1. Where are the two lighthouses?

_____

2. Which town is closest to the large ship?

_____

3. On which beach is there a lifeguard?

_____

4. Where can people keep their boats?

_____

5. Where is the largest school of whales?

_____

2 | Singular and Plural Nouns

Singular Nouns	Plural Nouns	Singular Nouns	Plural Nouns
cat	cat**s**	finch	finch**es**
dove	dove**s**	thrush	thrush**es**
walrus	walrus**es**	donkey	donkey**s**
fox	fox**es**	pony	pon**ies**

A. If the underlined noun is singular, write the plural form. If it is plural, write the singular form.

1. Aki visited the animals in the zoos.   _____

2. She watched the zebras gallop through the pass.   _____

3. The lynx cared for the baby.   _____

4. The monkey ate the bunch of bananas.   _____

5. Aki heard the crash when the chimp threw a pan. _____

6. Aki watched the lizards play around the cactus. _____

7. The parrot was picking the berry from the bush. _____

8. The jay sat on the perch.   _____

9. The fox slept in the small hutch.   _____

10. Aki told the class about her adventures.   _____

(continued)

LANGUAGE AND USAGE

2 | Singular and Plural Nouns *(continued from page 31)*

B. Writing Application: Sentences

You are a zoo keeper. Choose five kinds of animals in your zoo and write a sentence, telling what you will feed each of them tomorrow. Use the plural forms of five nouns from the box below.

fox	nuthatch	puppy	skunk
monkey	octopus	rhinoceros	snake

Enrichment

Write a table of contents for a book about animals. The title for each chapter should include the plural form of a noun from the box below. Be sure that each chapter has an interesting title!

jay	walrus	turkey	ostrich	fly
donkey	puppy	guppy	fox	thrush
monkey	bunny	pony	moth	panda

Table of Contents

	page
_____	5
_____	10
_____	17
_____	21
_____	25
_____	32
_____	36
_____	40

LANGUAGE AND USAGE

3 | More Plural Nouns

Singular Nouns	Plural Nouns	Singular Nouns	Plural Nouns
leaf	leav**es**	hero	hero**es**
giraffe	giraffe**s**	foot	feet
banjo	banjo**s**	deer	deer

A. Write the plural form of the noun in parentheses to complete each sentence. You may use your dictionary.

1. Opera lovers can listen to opera on their _____ . **(radio)**

2. Yesterday Murray heard some _____ sing. **(woman)**

3. They were _____ . **(soprano)**

4. Women with lower voices are called _____ . **(alto)**

5. Some _____ are tenors, and others are baritones. **(man)**

6. _____ sometimes sing in operas too. **(child)**

7. _____ and other instruments accompany the singers. **(piano)**

8. Murray reads about the _____ of opera stars. **(life)**

9. According to his _____ , they are the best singers. **(belief)**

10. He says some popular singers sound like _____ ! **(moose)**

11. He grits his _____ when he hears those singers. **(tooth)**

12. He likes opera singers to sing _____ . **(solo)**

13. He likes the _____ their voices make. **(echo)**

14. Murray finds many _____ to follow his interest. **(way)**

15. He hopes to visit some recording _____ . **(studio)**

16. He thinks that _____ reproduce music very well. **(stereo)**

17. His _____ are filled with records. **(shelf)**

18. Murray hopes to attend two opera _____ next year. **(series)**

(continued)

Level 5 Unit 3 Nouns   *(Use with pupil book pages 86–87.)*
Skill: Students will write the plural forms of irregular nouns.

LANGUAGE AND USAGE

3 | **More Plural Nouns** (continued from page 33)

B. Writing Application: A Paragraph

Write a paragraph about something you do or would like to do in your spare time. Use the plural forms of at least four nouns from the box below.

radio	shelf	banjo	hero	tooth
piano	life	studio	foot	stereo

★ Enrichment ★

Fabia Howl is writing rhyming word pairs for her new operetta. You can help her by combining the syllables in the notes to form nouns. Write the plural form of each noun next to its definition.

1. vegetables _____ , reddish fruits _____

2. singers _____ , singers _____

3. wireless sets _____ , artists' workrooms _____

4. brave persons _____ , numbers _____

5. musical instruments _____ , musical instruments _____

LANGUAGE AND USAGE

4 | Common and Proper Nouns

Common Nouns	Proper Nouns
ranger	Joe Garcia
place	Grand Canyon
month	June
holiday	Fourth of July

A. Underline the nouns in each group of sentences. Then write the proper nouns, using capital letters correctly. The numbers in parentheses tell how many common and proper nouns are in each group of sentences.

1. Last july my family visited banff national park in the province of alberta. banff is among the oldest parks in canada and covers more than 2500 square miles. **(9)**

_____

2. Our group camped near lake louise on the fourth of july and spent two afternoons at the lake. Many special exhibits and informative lectures were offered in the nearby lodge. **(8)**

_____

3. One day all of the visitors took a tour through cascade rock gardens. The guide was hilda revels. The hikers took a trail up sulphur mountain. The view from the top was spectacular. Later, miss revels pointed out the mountaintops. **(13)**

_____

4. In january people skate and ski in the mountains. Tourists can ride through the rocky mountains in a sleigh. **(6)**

_____

5. In june the springs and beautiful scenery attract travelers from the united states, europe, and even japan. **(7)**

_____

(continued)

Level 5   Unit 3 Nouns   *(Use with pupil book pages 88–89.)*
Skill: Students will identify common and proper nouns.

LANGUAGE AND USAGE

4 | **Common and Proper Nouns** *(continued from page 35)*

B. Writing Application: A Travel Poster

Make a poster to encourage people to visit your town. Draw a picture of a sight that would interest tourists. Then write five sentences on your poster, explaining why your town is interesting. Underline the common nouns on your poster. Circle the proper nouns.

★ Enrichment ★

Look at the meanings of the following symbols. Rewrite the paragraph below. Replace each symbol with the name of a person, a place, or a thing. Capitalize the proper nouns.

 a person   a place   a thing

So far the had gone well. I was proud to be testing my ☆ . I got to the 🏠 and saw the ☆ . Now I was getting nervous. Still I wanted the ☆ . There was no turning back. and 👤 had helped me before. Now it was my turn. I made it to the 🏠 , and there before me was the 🏠 . I heard a ☆ and then a ☆ . What was happening? I turned in time to see the ☆ coming from the 🏠 . I tried to do something, but my ☆ seemed frozen in fright. Suddenly I heard the voices of the 👤 behind me. What a ☆ !

_____

_____

_____

_____

_____

_____

LANGUAGE AND USAGE

5 | Singular Possessive Nouns

Singular Nouns	Singular Possessive Nouns
friend	**friend's** team
student	**student's** bat
Amos	**Amos's** decision

A. Rewrite each sentence. Change the underlined group of words to include a singular possessive noun.

1. The book belonging to Amos is on the first black player in the major leagues.

   _____

2. The name of this baseball player is Jackie Robinson.

   _____

3. The book is the autobiography of Robinson.

   _____

4. The playing of this second baseman attracted attention.

   _____

5. The average that this batter had was the highest in the league.

   _____

6. The skills that the athlete had earned him a place with the Dodgers.

   _____

7. The talents of the player won him the Spingarn Medal.

   _____

8. The election of the sports star to the Hall of Fame was in 1962.

   _____

(continued)

LANGUAGE AND USAGE

5 | Singular Possessive Nouns *(continued from page 37)*

B. Writing Application: A Paragraph

Write a paragraph about a real or an imaginary sports star. Explain why the star is famous. Include four or more singular possessive nouns in your paragraph.

Enrichment

Here is the equipment some students brought with them to play a new game called Jump Fast:

Explain how the students above will play Jump Fast, using the equipment they have with them. Write a possessive noun and another noun in each blank.

Jenny will hit _____ with _____ .

The ball will bounce over _____ . Amos must skip once

with _____ before Katie catches the ball

in _____ .

Now invent another game that can be played with the same equipment. On a separate piece of paper, explain how to play the game. Use singular possessive nouns in your explanation.

Level 5 Unit 3 Nouns *(Use with pupil book pages 90–91.)*
Skill: Students will write the possessive forms of singular nouns.

LANGUAGE AND USAGE

6 | Plural Possessive Nouns

Plural Nouns	Plural Possessive Nouns
bats	**bats'** wings
ladies	**ladies'** shoes
geese	**geese's** feathers
elk	**elk's** teeth

A. Rewrite each sentence. Change the underlined group of words to include a plural possessive noun.

1. <u>The names of the Marx brothers</u> were Groucho, Harpo, and Chico.

   _____

2. <u>The acting of the Marxes</u> was famous.

   _____

3. <u>The first public appearance the actors had</u> was on the stage.

   _____

4. <u>The jokes of the men</u> were funny.

   _____

5. Later, <u>movies by these heroes</u> were popular.

   _____

6. Perhaps <u>the favorite of the children</u> was Harpo.

   _____

7. Harpo and Chico played music in <u>the films of these stars</u>.

   _____

8. <u>The instruments these musicians owned</u> were a harp and a piano.

   _____

(continued)

LANGUAGE AND USAGE

6 | **Plural Possessive Nouns** (continued from page 39)

B. Writing Application: A Movie Review

Write five sentences about a movie that you have seen. Tell what the stars did. Explain why you did or did not like the movie. Include at least three plural possessive nouns in your review.

★ Enrichment ★

Hilda Highbrow is reviewing a new musical group. Help her write her review. Use the details in the picture to help you write the sentences. Use the word in parentheses and a plural possessive noun in each sentence.

1. (pianos) _____

2. (horns) _____

3. (harps) _____

4. (drums) _____

5. (violins) _____

Level 5 Unit 3 Nouns *(Use with pupil book pages 92–93.)*
Skill: Students will write the possessive forms of plural nouns.

COMPOSITION SKILL: INSTRUCTIONS

Main Idea of a Paragraph

A paragraph is made up of sentences that tell about one topic.
The sentences discuss one main idea about the topic.

Read the following paragraphs. Write the main idea of each paragraph in your own words. Draw a line through any sentence that does not tell about the main idea.

A.   When you can no longer tell what color your leather shoes are, it may be time to clean them. Most kids wear sneakers every day. Besides your dirty shoes, you will need a shoe brush, a soft cloth, and shoe polish. First, use the brush to remove any loose dirt from the shoes. Rain and snow are very bad for leather shoes. Then put some polish on the cloth and spread it evenly over the shoes. Rub the polish lightly into the leather. Finally, rub the shoes briskly with a clean, soft cloth until they shine.

Main Idea: _____

_____

_____

B.   What should you do if you are the only one to see a serious accident? If you think fast, you can help the injured person. The first thing to remember is to stay calm. If an adult is nearby, shout for help. If not, find a telephone and speak with the telephone operator. An operator's job must be exciting. Tell the operator your name, where you are, and what has happened. The operator will call the proper people for help. Go back to the person who is hurt and try to keep him or her calm until help arrives.

Main Idea: _____

_____

_____

Level 5 Unit 4 Instructions   *(Use with pupil book pages 122–123.)*
Skill: Students will identify the main idea of a paragraph and will identify sentences that do not tell about the main idea.

Topic Sentences and Supporting Details

> The **topic sentence** of a paragraph clearly states the main idea.
> The other sentences give **supporting details** about the main idea.

A. Each paragraph below needs a topic sentence. Read each paragraph and write two different topic sentences for it. Then put a check next to the topic sentence that you like better.

You can buy plant foods in liquid or in powder form. Carefully read the directions on the back of the container. Mix the food with water exactly as the directions tell you. You may harm your plants if you do not use the correct amount of plant food. Plants in clay pots usually need more plant food than those in plastic pots. Plants that sit or hang in a bright, sunny window need more food than those that are placed in a shadier spot. Feeding your plants once or twice a month is usually often enough. If the soil in a pot is white and crusty on top, you are feeding that plant too much.

Topic Sentence 1: _____

_____

Topic Sentence 2: _____

_____

Check all your plants often for insects. Even before buying a new plant, check for bugs. When you do bring a new plant home, set it apart from your other plants until you are sure it has no bugs. If you do find that some insects are living in your plants, separate affected plants from the others while you try to get rid of the bugs. You are less likely to have insects harm your plants if you keep the plants healthy and clean.

Topic Sentence 1: _____

_____

Topic Sentence 2: _____

_____

(continued)

COMPOSITION SKILL: INSTRUCTIONS

Topic Sentences and Supporting Details *(continued from page 42)*

B. Read each paragraph below. Think of supporting details you can add to each one. Then rewrite the paragraph, adding two or three more sentences with supporting details. Underline the topic sentence of each paragraph.

Fruit salad is delicious and easy to make. You can use almost any kind of fruit. Chopped nuts are good in it too. Cut up the fruit and put it in a large bowl. Add some fruit-flavored yogurt and stir everything together. Then cover the bowl and chill it until you are ready to eat. Yum!

_____

_____

_____

_____

_____

_____

_____

You can make your own rubber stamp. You will need a small block of wood, some thick rubber bands, scissors, a pencil, rubber cement, a stamp pad, and paper. First, draw a simple design on the woodblock with the pencil. Then cut pieces of rubber band to fit the outline of your design. Glue the rubber-band pieces in place, using the rubber cement. Now ink your stamp and try it on the paper.

_____

_____

_____

_____

_____

_____

_____

_____

COMPOSITION SKILL: INSTRUCTIONS

Step-by-Step Order

> When you write a paragraph of instructions, put the steps in an order that makes sense. Use order words such as *first, next, then,* and *finally* to help make the order clear.

A. The following paragraph gives instructions for making modeling dough. However, the instructions are all mixed up! Rewrite the paragraph, putting the instructions in order. Add order words to help make the order clear.

> Knead in food coloring. Put one cup of salt and one-half cup of cornstarch into a saucepan. Add two-thirds of a cup of water. Remove the pan from the heat. Cook over low heat, stirring constantly until the mixture becomes a thick mass. Cool the mixture until you can handle it easily. Use the dough immediately or put it into a covered jar and store it in the refrigerator.

_____

_____

_____

_____

_____

_____

_____

_____

_____

B. Now write a topic sentence for the paragraph of instructions you have just rewritten.

_____

_____

_____

COMPOSITION SKILL: INSTRUCTIONS

Purpose and Audience

> **Purpose** and **audience** affect what you say and how you say it.
> Some purposes for writing are to explain, to entertain, or to persuade.
> Some audiences are classmates, friends, teachers, and relatives.

Write the purpose and the audience for each of the following writing
situations.

1. Pam wrote a report about the American bald eagle for science class.

   Purpose: _____

   Audience: _____

2. Eric left a note on the refrigerator, asking his sister to please feed and walk the
dog for him that night.

   Purpose: _____

   Audience: _____

3. Becky's friend wanted to make balloon animals for some six-year-olds at a
birthday party. Becky wrote directions for her.

   Purpose: _____

   Audience: _____

4. Your letter about why children should be given free admission to local museums
appeared in your local newspaper.

   Purpose: _____

   Audience: _____

5. Matt wrote a story for his best friend about the funniest thing that ever happened to him.

   Purpose: _____

   Audience: _____

THE WRITING PROCESS: INSTRUCTIONS

Step 3: Revise

Have I	yes
added a topic sentence?	☐
circled sentences that are out of order and drawn arrows to show where they belong?	☐
added order words to make the order clearer?	☐
replaced unclear words with exact nouns?	☐

Revise the following instructions for making a terrarium. Use the check list above to help you. Check off each box when you have finished your revision.
• Use a thesaurus to choose exact words.
• Use the space above each line, on the sides, and below the paragraph for your changes.

You will need a large glass container with something tight to

cover it, pebbles, potting soil, and green plants that aren't very

big. Put a layer of pebbles in the bottom of the glass thing. Add

the potting soil. Moisten the soil until it is wet but not muddy.

Put something tight over the container. Place the plants in

firmly. Put your terrarium in a bright place, but not in the direct

sun. Now feel good about this small plant world.

Name _____

WORKBOOK
PLUS ▲ 47

THE WRITING PROCESS: INSTRUCTIONS

Step 4: Proofread

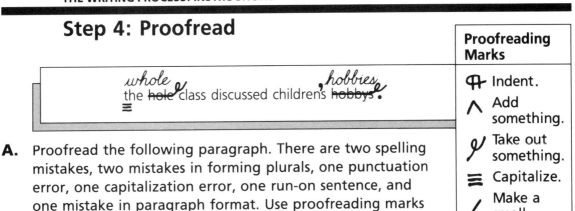

	Proofreading Marks
¶	Indent.
∧	Add something.
ℐ	Take out something.
≡	Capitalize.
/	Make a small letter.

A. Proofread the following paragraph. There are two spelling mistakes, two mistakes in forming plurals, one punctuation error, one capitalization error, one run-on sentence, and one mistake in paragraph format. Use proofreading marks to correct the mistakes. Use a dictionary to check your spelling.

You can make finger paint at home. Put one cup of laundry starch, one cup of cool water, and two cupes of hot water into a large saucepan. Cook over low heat until the mixture is thick turn off the stove. Add one cup of soap flaks to the saucepan. Stir well. The texture of the paint should be thick and smooth Divide the paint into for jars. stir some food coloring into each jar. Now your ready to paint!

B. Proofread the following paragraph. There are two spelling mistakes, two mistakes in forming plurals, one error in punctuation, one capitalization error, and one run-on sentence. Correct the mistakes.

Use your paints to make vegetable printes. Line a plate with several paper towels. Spread the paint evenly over the towels to make a stamp pad. add a few drops of liquid detergent to the paint slice some vegetables. For example, use potatos, mushrooms, or cabbage. Press the vegetable onto the stamp pad and then onto a peace of paper? Different vegetable shapes will make unusal designs.

Level 5 Unit 4 Instructions *(Use with pupil book pages 133–134.)*
Skill: Students will proofread paragraphs of instructions, correcting mistakes in spelling, capitalization, punctuation, formation of plurals, and paragraph format.

LANGUAGE AND USAGE

1 | Action Verbs

> Elizabeth **likes** art.
> Yesterday she **painted** a beautiful picture.

A. Write the action verb in each sentence.

1. Elizabeth went to an artist's studio. _____

2. She watched the artist carefully. _____

3. Elizabeth envied the potter's ability. _____

4. Elizabeth started a pottery club at school. _____

5. A different potter comes each week. _____

6. The potters instruct the students. _____

7. Elizabeth follows the instructions carefully. _____

8. First, she kneads the clay. _____

9. Then she throws a lump of clay onto the potter's wheel. _____

10. She slowly turns the heavy wheel with her foot. _____

11. Elizabeth wets her hands in a bowl of water. _____

12. Her fingers shape the clay. _____

13. She forms the clay into a mug. _____

14. Then she molds a piece of clay into a handle. _____

15. The students place the mugs in a special oven. _____

16. The clay bakes in the kiln for several hours. _____

17. Then the students put glaze on their mugs. _____

18. Some students paint designs on their work. _____

19. They return their mugs to the kiln. _____

20. The students display their work at the art fair. _____

(continued)

LANGUAGE AND USAGE

1 | **Action Verbs** *(continued from page 49)*

B. Writing Application: Instructions

Think of something you have made. It might be a painting, a model, or something you cooked. Write five sentences telling how you made it. Use an action verb in each sentence. Underline the action verbs.

★ Enrichment ★

The winner of each ticktacktoe game wrote three action verbs in a row. Find out who won each game. First, underline the action verbs in each game. Then write whether "X" or "O" won the game.

X cobra	O clean	O continent
X claim	O connect	X county
X cruel	O called	X chariot

1. The winner is _____ .

O system	X slither	X select
O suggest	X slender	X soar
O surrender	O society	X succeed

4. The winner is _____ .

O restless	O radish	O raisin
O runway	X rotten	O relate
X reacted	X require	X rushed

2. The winner is _____ .

X freckle	X fact	X forecast
O fade	O freeze	O fled
O full	X fantastic	O fourteen

5. The winner is _____ .

O afloat	O agree	X appreciate
X awkward	O assure	X auditorium
O ankle	O apply	X alphabet

3. The winner is _____ .

X mineral	X mistaken	O mosquito
O mild	O multiply	O massive
X murmur	X migrate	X mutter

6. The winner is _____ .

LANGUAGE AND USAGE

2 | Direct Objects

The students helped the **astronomers**.   *(helped whom?)*
Astronomers examine the **stars**.   *(examine what?)*
They observe **them** with telescopes.   *(observe what?)*

A. Underline the action verb in each sentence. Write the direct object.

1. Maria Mitchell studied the stars.   _____

2. As a child, she helped her father with his work.   _____

3. Her father encouraged his daughter.   _____

4. At the age of twelve, she observed an eclipse.   _____

5. After that she increased her knowledge.   _____

6. She watched the sky at night through a telescope.   _____

7. She read many books about astronomy.   _____

8. In 1847 Maria Mitchell discovered a comet.   _____

9. She gained fame through this discovery.   _____

10. The King of Denmark honored Mitchell.   _____

11. She won a gold medal.   _____

12. The American Academy of Arts and Sciences elected her
    as a member.   _____

13. As the first female member, she paved the way for
    others.   _____

14. Vassar College hired the scientist.   _____

15. She continued her work in astronomy.   _____

16. Mitchell taught it as a subject.   _____

17. She helped her students with research.   _____

18. As a teacher, Mitchell influenced future astronomers.   _____

(continued)

LANGUAGE AND USAGE

2 | **Direct Objects** *(continued from page 51)*

B. Writing Application: A Post Card

You have just landed on the moon. Write a post card to a friend, telling what you have found there. Use at least three action verbs and three direct objects. Circle the direct objects.

Enrichment

This newspaper story tells about an important discovery. What is it? Explain by completing each sentence below with a direct object.

NEWS SERVICE NATIONAL 20:80:08   7-15

Dr. Carmelita Sanchez discovered a _____ today.

She was working in her laboratory when she suddenly noticed a _____

_____ . She grabbed her _____

and checked the _____ .

Dr. Sanchez tested the _____ . First, she dropped

_____ into water. Then she inspected the _____

_____ . Nothing had changed. She tried a _____

_____ . It didn't work. Finally, she tried _____

_____ . It changed the _____ .

She had completed her _____ .

Her assistants helped _____ . They repeated

the _____ . They proved the _____ .

Officials praise _____ . They say that the discovery

aids _____ . Dr. Sanchez received a _____

_____ for her accomplishment.

3 | Main Verbs and Helping Verbs

> helping   main
> verb   verb
> My parents **have left** for the bookstore.
>
> helping   main
> verb   verb
> They **are going** to the annual book sale.

A. Write the verb or the verb phrase in each sentence. For each verb phrase, underline the helping verb once and the main verb twice.

1. Our local bookstore is celebrating Mark Twain's birthday.

   _____

2. The store has lowered the prices of all its books.

   _____

3. Already, sales have broken all records. _____

4. Yesterday my parents planned their purchases.

   _____

5. They are buying many books for gifts.

   _____

6. I am looking for a book by Mark Twain.

   _____

7. However, Mark Twain's books were selling quickly all morning.

   _____

8. Many copies of my favorite books had disappeared by noon.

   _____

9. The clerks were piling other books on the tables.

   _____

10. I will get there earlier next year. _____

(continued)

Level 5 Unit 5 Verbs   *(Use with pupil book pages 146–147.)*
Skill: Students will identify main verbs and helping verbs.

3 | **Main Verbs and Helping Verbs** *(continued from page 53)*

B. Writing Application: Sentences

Write five sentences, telling about a visit that you made to a library or a book-store. Use a main verb and a helping verb in each sentence.

═ Enrichment ═

The first sentence of a story is very important. Read these first sentences. Underline the main verb and the helping verb in each sentence.

''Nothing had gone right that day.''

''The mysterious woman and her package had disappeared.''

''As usual the twins were arguing with each other.''

Now write your own first sentence for each of the stories below. Use a main verb and a helping verb in each sentence.

1. **A story about a gas station:** _____

   _____

2. **A story about space travel:** _____

   _____

3. **A story about your school:** _____

   _____

4. **A story about your relatives:** _____

   _____

5. **A story about the future:** _____

   _____

6. **A story about a sports star:** _____

   _____

7. **A story about rock music:** _____

   _____

LANGUAGE AND USAGE

4 | Linking Verbs

> **Linking Verbs:** Hawaii's nickname **is** the Aloha State.
>
> Hawaii **looks** beautiful.
>
> **Action Verbs:** The tourist **looks** at the map of Hawaii.
>
> The map **shows** many tourist attractions.

A. Write the verb in each sentence. Label each verb *linking* or *action.*

1. Hawaii is the youngest state in the United States.

   _____

2. Hawaii's attractions are famous.

   _____

3. To a visitor, these islands look spectacular.

   _____

4. The mild climate feels perfect.

   _____

5. Visitors feel the warm sun and the cool ocean breezes.

   _____

6. They enjoy the warm waters of the Pacific Ocean.

   _____

B. Underline the linking verb in each sentence. Draw an arrow showing the words that the verb links.

7. Farm products are a source of income for Hawaiians.

8. Foreign markets seem interested in the islands' many crops.

9. Sugar cane is Hawaii's most important product.

10. Pineapples are its second largest crop.

11. Other fruits appear plentiful on the islands as well.

12. The air smells sweet with the scent of coconuts and bananas.

(continued)

LANGUAGE AND USAGE

4 | **Linking Verbs**   (continued from page 55)

C. Writing Application: A Description

Write five sentences, describing your state, province, or city. Use a linking verb from the box below in each sentence.

am	is	are	was	were	will be
look	feel	taste	smell	seem	appear

★ Enrichment ★

Pretend that you are visiting the imaginary tropical island of Tralala. Complete the following sentences about the island. Write a linking verb in each box. Then add words that name or describe the subject of the sentence.

1. The climate of this island [   ] _____

    _____ .

2. The flowers here [   ] _____

    _____ .

3. The animals on the island [   ] _____

    _____ .

4. Strange fruits [   ] _____

    _____ .

5. Several bubbling streams [   ] _____

    _____ .

6. The people on this island [   ] _____

    _____ .

7. A huge bird [   ] _____

    _____ .

LANGUAGE AND USAGE

5 | Present Tense

George **enjoys** cooking.	We **enjoy** cooking.
He **guesses** the ingredients.	You **guess** the ingredients.
The chef **coaches** George.	Both chefs **coach** George.
Cool air **refreshes** him.	These two fans **refresh** him.
Cooking **relaxes** George.	George and the chef **relax**.
He **tries** new recipes.	I **try** new recipes.

A. Write the correct present tense form of each verb in parentheses.

1. My brother Pete _____ wonderful meals. **(fix)**

2. He _____ time and care. **(take)**

3. I _____ Pete. **(watch)**

4. He _____ the tomatoes to see if they are ripe. **(pinch)**

5. He _____ the lettuce. **(wash)**

6. Then he _____ it carefully. **(dry)**

7. He _____ oil and vinegar to make salad dressing. **(mix)**

8. The timer _____ . **(buzz)**

9. My sisters _____ into the kitchen. **(rush)**

10. Pete _____ the dinner. **(serve)**

11. His stew _____ delicious. **(look)**

12. We all _____ the dinner. **(enjoy)**

13. After dinner we _____ the clean-up duty. **(discuss)**

14. Pete _____ of a number between one and ten. **(think)**

15. We each _____ a number. **(guess)**

16. My number _____ the closest to Pete's. **(come)**

17. "You _____ !" my sisters shout gleefully. **(win)**

18. I _____ to clear the dirty dishes. **(begin)**

(continued)

Level 5 Unit 5 Verbs *(Use with pupil book pages 150–151.)*
Skill: Students will use present tense verbs correctly with singular and plural subjects.

Name _____

LANGUAGE AND USAGE

5 | **Present Tense** (continued from page 57)

B. Writing Application: A Progress Report

The Parents' Association has hired the students in your class to prepare a special luncheon. Students are busy preparing the food, setting up the room, and putting up decorations. You are in charge of the event. Write a progress report for the Parents' Association. Use the present tense form of five verbs from the box below.

| arrange | push | carry | toss | fix | scrub | reach | make |

Enrichment

Classroom Cookery, a television show, is captioned for people who have difficulty hearing. Below are scenes from four different shows. Explain what is happening in each scene by completing the caption below each picture. Use a verb in the present tense form in each sentence.

1. Cecil and Ron _____

_____ .

3. Ming Chen _____

_____ .

2. He _____

_____ .

4. The girls _____

_____ .

LANGUAGE AND USAGE

6 | Past Tense

> Eric **watched** the workers.
> He **saved** his questions for later.
> The workers **stayed** for a long time.
> Then they **hurried** to the next job.
> They **scrubbed** the kettles thoroughly.

A. Complete each sentence by writing the past tense form of the verb in parentheses.

1. Eric _____ his visit to Williamsburg. (**enjoy**)

2. He _____ about the colonists. (**learn**)

3. He _____ some of the colonists' crafts. (**observe**)

4. The colonists _____ their own soap. (**produce**)

5. Women _____ wood ashes from their fireplaces. (**collect**)

6. Their cooking _____ fats and grease. (**supply**)

7. The women _____ the ashes to a large barrel. (**carry**)

8. They _____ water through the ashes in the barrel. (**pour**)

9. It _____ out through a hole near the bottom. (**drip**)

10. The ashes _____ the water to turn brown. (**cause**)

11. The brown liquid _____ into a pail. (**drop**)

12. People _____ this liquid lye. (**call**)

13. The women _____ the lye in a kettle. (**place**)

14. They _____ the fats and the grease. (**add**)

15. The mixture _____ slowly. (**boil**)

16. After a while, the mixture _____ into a jelly. (**turn**)

17. People _____ this jellylike substance. (**store**)

18. They _____ the soft and smelly substance for soap. (**use**)

(continued)

Level 5 **Unit 5 Verbs** *(Use with pupil book pages 152–153.)*
Skill: Students will form the past tense of regular verbs.

LANGUAGE AND USAGE

6 | **Past Tense** *(continued from page 59)*

B. Writing Application: A Paragraph

A time machine has taken you back to the time of the North American colonists. Now you have returned to the present. Write a paragraph, telling your friends about what you saw. Use at least five past tense verbs. Circle the verbs.

Enrichment

The year is 2588. You have just returned from a time-machine trip back to 1988. While you were on your trip, you took pictures of the machines that people used in 1988. Explain how the people used these machines. Write a sentence for each picture. Use a different past tense verb in each sentence.

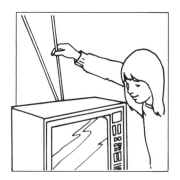

_____

_____

_____

_____

LANGUAGE AND USAGE

7 | Future Tense

We **shall stay** here this summer.
My brother **will work** next July.

A. Underline the verb or verb phrase in each sentence. Then rewrite each sentence, using the future tense form of the underlined verb.

1. This summer Eva has traveled to New Mexico.

   _____

2. Each year she visits her Aunt Nina, who is a scientist.

   _____

3. Eva helps with the research.

   _____

4. They work at a large pueblo ruin.

   _____

5. They have traced the development of the pueblo.

   _____

6. The scientists have used the latest research techniques.

   _____

7. Their findings have provided information about the Mimbres people.

   _____

8. Aunt Nina and Eva dig with care.

   _____

9. They search for Mimbres pottery.

   _____

10. Eva has learned much about archaeology.

    _____

(continued)

LANGUAGE AND USAGE

7 | **Future Tense** *(continued from page 61)*

B. Writing Application: A Paragraph

Write a paragraph, describing your plans for next summer. Your plans can be real or imaginary. Use a future tense verb in each sentence. Underline each verb.

Enrichment

The symbols below are taken from an ancient Egyptian form of writing called hieroglyphics. Scientists often find this kind of writing in Egyptian ruins. Use the meanings of the symbols to write a sentence for each group of symbols below. Use a future tense verb in each sentence.

person   see   woods, tree   write

cut, knife   plants   buildings   animals

foreign country   water   go, walk   books, paintings

eat, speak   food   boat, sail   steps, climb

1. _____

2. _____

3. _____

4. _____

5. _____

6. _____

Now draw two hieroglyphic sentences of your own. Then write each sentence, using a future tense verb.

7. _____

8. _____

Level 5 Unit 5 Verbs *(Use with pupil book pages 154–155.)*
Skill: Students will write the future tense forms of verbs.

Name _____

LANGUAGE AND USAGE

8 | Subject-Verb Agreement

Singular Subjects	Plural Subjects	*I* or *you*
Cleo **rides** the bus.	The girls **ride** the bus.	You **ride** the bus.
She **enjoys** the ride.	We **enjoy** the ride.	I **enjoy** the ride.
My brother **catches** the bus.	Cleo and I **catch** the bus.	You **catch** the bus.

A. Rewrite each sentence, using the correct present tense form of the verb in parentheses.

1. My brother __?__ for the government. (**work**)

   _____

2. He __?__ public transportation. (**plan**)

   _____

3. Public transportation __?__ trains, subways, and buses. (**include**)

   _____

4. It __?__ people and the environment. (**help**)

   _____

5. My brother and I __?__ problems in public transportation. (**discuss**)

   _____

6. We __?__ about the increase in automobile traffic. (**talk**)

   _____

7. The roads __?__ more crowded each year. (**become**)

   _____

8. My brother and other workers __?__ different solutions. (**try**)

   _____

9. They __?__ the use of public transportation. (**encourage**)

   _____

10. Now I __?__ the bus whenever possible. (**ride**)

    _____

(continued)

Level 5 Unit 5 Verbs *(Use with pupil book pages 156–157.)*
Skill: Students will write verbs that agree with singular and plural subjects.

LANGUAGE AND USAGE

8 | **Subject-Verb Agreement** *(continued from page 63)*

B. Writing Application: A Travel Diary

You and a friend are taking a trip by bus, car, or train. Write at least five sentences for your diary, telling about what happens on the journey. Use the present tense form of a verb in each sentence. Make sure each verb agrees with its subject.

Enrichment

Read the bus schedule below and answer the questions that follow. Each answer should be a complete sentence that uses a verb in the present tense form. Try to use a different subject for each sentence.

	ARRIVES				
	COBURN	TYVILLE	MAXTON	SIMPSON	JEROME
LEAVES	9:30 A.M.	10:00 A.M.	10:10 A.M.	10:15 A.M.	10:20 A.M.
	11:00 A.M.	11:30 A.M.	11:40 A.M.	11:45 A.M.	11:50 A.M.
	1:30 P.M.	2:00 P.M.	2:10 P.M.	2:15 P.M.	2:20 P.M.

1. When does the first bus leave Coburn in the morning?

   _____

2. When does the 1:30 P.M. bus arrive in Tyville?

   _____

3. What time do I get to Maxton if I take the 11:00 A.M. bus?

   _____

4. Which two stops come between Tyville and Jerome?

   _____

5. What do people call the last stop on the line?

   _____

6. How do I get to Simpson before 10:30 A.M.?

   _____

LANGUAGE AND USAGE

9 | Agreement with *be* and *have*

Subjects	Forms of *be*	Forms of *have*
I	am, was	have, had
he, she, it	is, was	has, had
singular nouns	is, was	has, had
you, we, they	are, were	have, had
plural nouns	are, were	have, had

A. The underlined verb in each sentence does not agree with its subject. Rewrite each sentence correctly.

1. <u>Has</u> you ever built a model airplane?

    _____

2. I <u>is</u> building one now.

    _____

3. It <u>are</u> a free-flight model with no wires.

    _____

4. Most free-flight models <u>is</u> made from balsa wood.

    _____

5. This model <u>have</u> a wingspan of six feet.

    _____

6. Grandfather <u>have</u> given me advice on it.

    _____

7. He <u>were</u> once an airline pilot.

    _____

8. We <u>was</u> planning to use a piston engine for power.

    _____

9. Grandfather and I <u>is</u> entering an air show this year.

    _____

10. I <u>were</u> too young to enter last year.

    _____

(continued)

LANGUAGE AND USAGE

9 | **Agreement with *be* and *have*** *(continued from page 65)*

B. Writing Application: Creative Writing

Imagine that you are so small that you can fit into a model plane. Write a paragraph about a trip you take. Use forms of *be* and *have* in your sentences. Make sure that the verbs agree with their subjects.

★ Enrichment ★

Captain Chang's plane has encountered rough weather. She has radioed for help, but static has made parts of the air traffic controller's answer impossible to understand. Help Captain Chang by rewriting the answer. Use a form of *be* or *have* wherever you run into static!

Roger, Flight 555. We ∿∿∿ you on radar. We ∿∿∿ reading you, and your request ∿∿∿ been received. The weather you ∿∿∿ experiencing ∿∿∿ a low-pressure area stretching from Springdale to Winter Valley. The storm ∿∿∿ moving at twenty-five miles per hour due east. You ∿∿∿ passed the center of the storm and ∿∿∿ out of danger. We ∿∿∿ routing you through Summerville, however, because another storm front ∿∿∿ approached from the north. At present your altitude ∿∿∿ holding steady. It looks as if the worst ∿∿∿ over. We ∿∿∿ transferred you to air traffic control at Summerville. Good luck. Over.

_____

_____

_____

_____

_____

_____

_____

_____

_____

_____

LANGUAGE AND USAGE

10 | Contractions with *not*

Verb + *not*	Contraction	Verb + *not*	Contraction
do not	don't	has not	hasn't
did not	didn't	had not	hadn't
is not	isn't	would not	wouldn't
were not	weren't	cannot	can't
will not	won't	must not	mustn't

A. Write the contraction for each underlined word or words.

1. Max, I <u>cannot</u> go to the concert with you. _____

2. Are you <u>not</u> feeling well? _____

3. I <u>do not</u> have my science report finished yet. _____

4. Dad <u>will not</u> let me go until it is done. _____

5. The report <u>is not</u> due until next week. _____

6. I <u>could not</u> work on it over the weekend. _____

7. It <u>has not</u> even been started yet! _____

8. I <u>had not</u> done my research until this week. _____

9. I <u>did not</u> know it would take this much time. _____

B. Write the words that were combined to form the contraction in each sentence.

10. I wasn't the only person going with you, I hope. _____

11. No, you weren't. Josh is coming too. _____

12. Well, that doesn't seem so bad. _____

13. I wouldn't want to spoil your fun. _____

14. You mustn't worry about that. _____

15. A concert shouldn't interfere with your schoolwork. _____

16. I didn't want to ruin everything. _____

17. You haven't, but I wish you could go. _____

18. Next time I won't wait until the last minute. _____

(continued)

Level 5 Unit 5 Verbs *(Use with pupil book pages 160–161.)*
Skill: Students will identify and will write contractions.

LANGUAGE AND USAGE

10 | **Contractions with *not*** *(continued from page 67)*

C. Writing Application: A Letter

You were supposed to go somewhere with a friend, and now you find that you are unable to go. Write a letter of apology, explaining what has happened. Include at least five contractions that use the word *not*.

★ Enrichment ★

You are writing a science report on safety. Write two sentences that tell about each picture set. In the first sentence, tell what to do. In the second sentence, tell what not to do. Use a different contraction in the second sentence of each pair.

                   YES   **NO**

1.

        _____

        _____

        _____

2.

        _____

        _____

        _____

3.

        _____

        _____

        _____

4.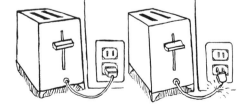

        _____

        _____

        _____

LANGUAGE AND USAGE

11 | Regular and Irregular Verbs

	Verb	**Past Tense**	**Past with Helping Verb**
Regular Verbs:	paint	painted	(has, have, had) painted
	hire	hired	(has, have, had) hired
	spy	spied	(has, have, had) spied
Irregular Verbs:	go	went	(has, have, had) gone
	think	thought	(has, have, had) thought

A. In the first column, write the past tense form of each underlined verb. In the second column, write the past form of the verb when it is used with a helping verb.

1. We start a class newspaper. _____ have _____

2. We go to the newspaper office. _____ had _____

3. We come back with good ideas. _____ had _____

4. We try them out. _____ have _____

5. Eduardo brings his camera. _____ has _____

6. He uses it a lot. _____ has _____

7. He takes good pictures. _____ has _____

8. He makes copies of the photographs. _____ has _____

9. He wants a career as a photographer. _____ had _____

10. He says so to his friends. _____ has _____

11. Doreen thinks differently. _____ has _____

12. She hopes to be a writer. _____ had _____

13. She always carries a pad with her. _____ had _____

14. She writes articles for the paper. _____ has _____

15. Several of her articles run in it. _____ have _____

16. Eduardo and Doreen cover sports. _____ have _____

17. They report on every game. _____ have _____

18. Doreen interviews the players. _____ had _____

(continued)

Level 5 Unit 5 Verbs *(Use with pupil book pages 162–163.)*
Skill: Students will write the past and past participle forms of regular and irregular verbs.

LANGUAGE AND USAGE

11 | Regular and Irregular Verbs *(continued from page 69)*

B. Writing Application: A Job Application

You are applying for a job as either a newspaper photographer or reporter. Write five sentences about pictures that you have taken or articles that you have written. Use past forms of five of the verbs from the box below.

> bring   come   go   make   say   take   think   write

 Enrichment

Nina Newsworthy is interviewing two candidates for class president. Help Nina finish her interview. Complete each candidate's answers. Use a past form of a verb from the box in each of your answers.

> run   bring   come   go   make   say   take   think   write

Nina: What schools have you attended in the past?

Candidate 1: I have _____ .

Candidate 2: I _____ .

Nina: Have you ever run for a class office before?

Candidate 1: I have _____ .

Candidate 2: I _____ .

Nina: What class projects have you been involved in?

Candidate 1: I _____ .

Candidate 2: I have _____ .

Nina: What do you think the class has accomplished in the past year?

Candidate 1: The class _____ .

Candidate 2: We have _____ .

Nina: What should be the class's major concern for next year?

Candidate 1: I _____ .

Candidate 2: I have _____ .

LANGUAGE AND USAGE

12 | More Irregular Verbs

Verb	Past Tense	Past with Helping Verb
sing	sang	(has, have, had) sung
begin	began	(has, have, had) begun
wear	wore	(has, have, had) worn
choose	chose	(has, have, had) chosen
grow	grew	(has, have, had) grown

A. Rewrite each sentence. Use the correct past form of the verb in parentheses.

1. Ivan __?__ a glance at the thermometer. (**steal**)

   _____

2. He had __?__ winter was coming. (**know**)

   _____

3. It __?__ with the first cold spell. (**begin**)

   _____

4. That morning in October, he had __?__ in the pond. (**swim**)

   _____

5. In the afternoon, it had __?__ cold. (**grow**)

   _____

6. Ivan __?__ a sweater for the first time in months. (**wear**)

   _____

7. Since then the water in the pond has __?__ . (**freeze**)

   _____

8. The wind has __?__ the leaves from the trees. (**blow**)

   _____

9. Many of the birds __?__ south weeks ago. (**fly**)

   _____

10. Only the cardinals and the blue jays have __?__ to stay. (**choose**)

   _____

(continued)

12 | **More Irregular Verbs** *(continued from page 71)*

B. Writing Application: Sentences

Write five sentences about how you once knew that spring was coming. In each sentence, use a past form of one of the verbs from the box below.

sing	begin	blow	know
swim	wear	grow	fly

★ Enrichment ★

Write six alphabet sentences. Use a past form of a verb from the box below. Then write a sentence, using words that begin with the same letter as the verb. Each sentence must have at least four words. The first sentence has been done for you.

ring	begin	break	freeze	fly
swim	wear	choose	grow	tear

1. <u>Five flocks of feathered finch had flown from the forest.</u>

2. _____

_____

3. _____

_____

4. _____

_____

5. _____

_____

6. _____

_____

Level 5 Unit 5 Verbs *(Use with pupil book pages 164–165.)*
Skill: Students will write the past and past participle forms of irregular verbs.

LANGUAGE AND USAGE

13 | Verb Phrases with *have*

Verb Phrases	Verb Phrases with Contractions
I **could have tried** to go.	I **could've tried** to go.
You **would have enjoyed** the day.	You **would've enjoyed** the day.
We **should have packed** a picnic.	We **should've packed** a picnic.
She **must have seen** the float.	She **must've seen** the float.

A. Rewrite the verb phrase in each sentence so that it includes a contraction.

1. You should have seen that parade! _____

2. I could have gotten there earlier. _____

3. It must have been a good one. _____

4. I could have left my house earlier. _____

5. I should have remembered the time. _____

6. You would have liked our float. _____

7. I could have taken a picture of it for you. _____

8. People must have come from miles away. _____

9. The children would have watched the show
   all day. _____

10. They must have stayed for at least two hours. _____

B. Write the verb phrase in each sentence so that it does not include a contraction.
If the verb phrase is incorrect, write it correctly.

11. You should've seen my mother in the band. _____

12. Her music would of amazed you. _____

13. She must've practiced for months. _____

14. She could of passed for a professional musician. _____

15. The band should've had more time. _____

16. They must of been the best act in the parade. _____

(continued)

Level 5   Unit 5   Verbs   *(Use with pupil book pages 166–167.)*
Skill: Students will identify and will write verb phrases with *have.*

LANGUAGE AND USAGE

13 | **Verb Phrases with *have*** (continued from page 73)

C. Writing Application: Sentences

Imagine that you were once a clown in a parade. Write six sentences about your act. Use a different verb phrase with *have* in each sentence.

★ Enrichment ★

The members of the Nature Club are having problems making their float. Help them by writing a solution to each problem shown in the pictures below. Try to use a different verb phrase with *have* or *'ve* in each sentence.

_____

_____

_____

_____

LANGUAGE AND USAGE

14 | *teach, learn; let, leave*

> Will you **teach** me about camps?
> I would like to **learn** how to find a good one.
> Will your mother **let** you go?
> She said I could **leave** for camp next summer.
> I must **leave** my dog at home.

A. Complete each sentence with the correct word in parentheses.

1. Mr. Berg will _____ us about camping. (**teach, learn**)

2. Students will _____ about many kinds of camps. (**teach, learn**)

3. Leaders _____ the campers many useful things. (**teach, learn**)

4. They _____ the campers work independently. (**let, leave**)

5. Campers _____ to do things on their own. (**teach, learn**)

6. Some campers _____ home in the summer. (**let, leave**)

7. Their parents _____ them go to overnight camp. (**let, leave**)

8. They _____ their families behind. (**let, leave**)

9. At camp they _____ how to live outdoors. (**teach, learn**)

10. Eric will _____ for camp next July. (**let, leave**)

11. His parents will _____ him go for two weeks. (**let, leave**)

12. His sister will _____ him borrow her camera. (**let, leave**)

13. A volunteer will _____ him to take pictures. (**teach, learn**)

14. Eric will _____ other skills too. (**teach, learn**)

15. The staff will _____ him to swim and to sail. (**teach, learn**)

16. Eric's brother will _____ him use his sleeping bag. (**let, leave**)

17. Eric hates to _____ his relatives at home. (**let, leave**)

18. However, he will _____ a lot at camp. (**teach, learn**)

(continued)

LANGUAGE AND USAGE

14 | *teach, learn; let, leave* (continued from page 75)

B. Writing Application: A Letter

Pretend that you are at summer camp. Write a letter to your relatives at home. Tell them what you are doing. Use the verbs *teach, learn, let,* and *leave*.

★ Enrichment ★

It is visiting day at camp. Use the map below to answer the visitors' questions. Write a complete sentence for each answer. Use the words *teach, learn, let,* and *leave* in your answers.

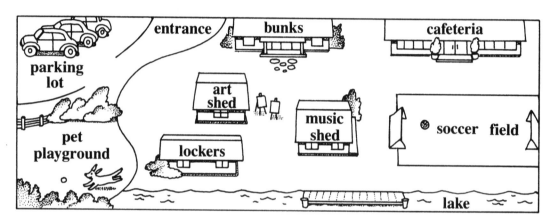

1. Where do I park my car?

   _____

2. Where can my dog run?

   _____

3. Where can we sing the new camp song?

   _____

4. Where can I watch the coach instructing the soccer team?

   _____

Now write one more question a visitor might ask. Then write your answer, using the verb *teach, learn, let,* or *leave*.

5. _____

   _____

Level 5 Unit 5 Verbs   *(Use with pupil book pages 168–169.)*
Skill: Students will use *teach, learn, let,* and *leave* correctly.

LANGUAGE AND USAGE

15 | *sit, set; can, may*

> I **sit** in a big, comfortable chair.
> I **set** my appointment card on the front desk.
> I **can** hear the dentist's drill.
> **May** I go home now?

A. One verb in each sentence is used incorrectly. Rewrite each sentence correctly.

1. Please set in the waiting room until the dentist is ready.

   _____

2. You can come in now.

   _____

3. Set in the large chair by the sink.

   _____

4. Sit your books on the table by the window.

   _____

5. May you lean back a little farther?

   _____

6. May you feel the cavity in that molar?

   _____

7. You'll have to sit a date to have it filled.

   _____

8. Can I finish cleaning your teeth now?

   _____

9. You can rinse out your mouth now.

   _____

10. You may set up now that we're finished.

    _____

(continued)

Level 5 Unit 5 Verbs   *(Use with pupil book pages 170–171.)*
Skill: Students will use *sit, set, can,* and *may* correctly.

LANGUAGE AND USAGE

15 | *sit, set; can, may*   (continued from page 77)

B. Writing Application: Instructions

Write six instructions a dentist might give you for taking care of your teeth. Include the verbs *sit*, *set*, *can*, and *may* in your instructions.

★ Enrichment ★

The inventors of the machines below thought that their inventions would help people take care of their teeth. The only problem was that no one could figure out how to use them. Write two sentences of instructions for each invention. Use the verb *sit*, *set*, *can*, or *may* in each sentence.

1. Max Grogl invented a switch that turns off the dentist's drill when the patient wants to say "ouch."

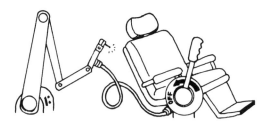

_____

_____

_____

_____

2. Martina Vesper invented the combination toothbrush-radio that makes brushing your teeth more fun.

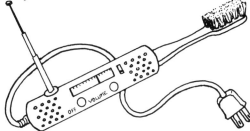

_____

_____

_____

_____

Now draw your own dental invention. Write two sentences that tell about it.

_____

_____

_____

_____

COMPOSITION SKILL: STORY

Plot

> There are three main parts to a **plot**. The **beginning** starts with a problem. The **middle** tells what happens as a result of the opening situation. The **end** tells how the problem and its resulting complications are solved.

Think of a story you have read. Write a plot outline of the story. Write only the main points of each part. Leave out the details.

Beginning: _____

_____

_____

_____

Middle: _____

_____

_____

_____

_____

_____

_____

_____

_____

_____

End: _____

_____

_____

_____

_____

Setting and Characters

> The **setting** is the time and the place of a story. The **characters** are the people, the animals, or the imaginary creatures in a story.

A. Choose one of the story settings below. Write five sentences that show rather than tell about the setting.

1. Inside the world's tallest building just after it is completed
2. A cattle ranch in the Southwest during the hottest part of the year
3. A big city, one hundred years from now
4. A school playground on the first day of the school year

_____

_____

_____

_____

_____

_____

_____

_____

B. Think of your own setting for a story. Write at least five sentences that show rather than tell about the setting.

_____

_____

_____

_____

_____

_____

_____

_____

(continued)

COMPOSITION SKILL: STORY

Setting and Characters *(continued from page 80)*

C. Choose one of the story settings that you described on page 89. Then think about two characters who might appear in a story with that setting. Describe each character by writing two sentences to answer each question below.

Character 1:

1. What does Character 1 think and do? _____

_____

_____

2. What does Character 1 tell about Character 2? _____

_____

_____

Character 2:

3. What does Character 2 think and do? _____

_____

_____

4. What does Character 2 tell about Character 1? _____

_____

_____

D. Now write a dialogue between your two characters. Write at least four sentences. Show what each character is like by what each one says.

_____

_____

_____

_____

_____

_____

_____

Step 3: Revise

Have I	yes
checked that the story has a plot and added to the middle so the plot makes sense?	☐
added details to help describe the setting?	☐
added dialogue to show what the characters are like?	☐
changed the tenses of some verbs so that all verbs are in the same tense?	☐

Revise the following story. Use the check list above to help you. Check off each box when you have finished your revision.

• Use the space above each line, on the sides, and below the story for your changes.

The Case of the Missing Bicycle

Once upon a time, ten-year-old Detective Jones was sitting in

his messy office when a little boy burst through the door. He

had a problem. He is very upset.

Detective Jones calmed him down. He talked to the little

boy. He listened very carefully. He took notes in a little black

book. Then Detective Jones looked for clues. He found some.

Then he found the bicycle in an old shack. Tommy is

happy. Detective Jones is pleased.

"Another case solved, another client satisfied," he says as

he returns to his office.

THE WRITING PROCESS: STORY

Step 4: Proofread

should've tried
i ~~should of tryed~~ harder.

Proofread the following paragraphs. There are three spelling errors, four punctuation errors, two run-on sentences, and two mistakes in paragraph format. There are also four errors in capitalization and three errors in forming contractions. Use proofreading marks to correct the mistakes. Use a dictionary to check your spelling.

Mr. and Mrs. Hall decided that their childern, Anna and Georgie, needed a pet. The family went to a pet store and looked at different animals They could of selected a dog or a cat, but they didnt. Instead, they carried home a strange bird it was a foot tall and had three fuzzy blue feathers on its head, a big orange beak, and green wings. they finalely named it Harold. Harold could do many amazing tricks. He knew words in seven languages He could also turn on the radio with his beak, and he loved to swoop down and pick up objects off the ground. Soon strange things began to happen. One of anna's friends said a shrill voice speaking japanese had been answering the Halls' telephone? Then the police called they said neighbors had complained about loud music coming from the apartment during the day. Something had to be done.

''We should of gotten a big cage for Harold,'' sighed Mrs. hall

LANGUAGE AND USAGE

1 | What Is an Adjective?

> **What Kind:** **Nervous, impatient** travelers stood at the rail.
> They were **weary** and **hungry**.
> **How Many:** **Many** immigrants had come before them.

A. Write each adjective and the noun or the pronoun that it describes. Do not include *a, an,* or *the.*

1. A single ship moved toward the bustling harbor.

   _____

2. It was noisy and crowded.

   _____

3. Many adults were happy and talkative.

   _____

4. They were eager to reach the final destination.

   _____

5. Two small girls peered toward the distant land.

   _____

6. They were curious about the future.

   _____

7. Would they like living in the large, strange country?

   _____

8. Suddenly they heard several joyous shouts.

   _____

9. An enormous, majestic statue appeared on the horizon.

   _____

10. The brilliant torch welcomed the travelers to a new home.

    _____

(continued)

What Is an Adjective?   *(continued from page 85)*

B. Writing Application: A Description

You and your family are moving to a new country. Imagine what your new home will be like. Write at least five sentences, describing your new home. Use two adjectives in each sentence.

Enrichment

Printed below are the words *The Statue of Liberty.* On the line next to each letter, write a group of words consisting of one noun or pronoun and at least two adjectives. Every word should begin with the letter at the beginning of the line. The first one has been done for you.

T   twelve timid travelers _____

H   _____

E   _____

S   _____

T   _____

A   _____

T   _____

U   _____

E   _____

O   _____

F   _____

L   _____

I   _____

B   _____

E   _____

R   _____

T   _____

Y   _____

LANGUAGE AND USAGE

2 | Articles and Demonstrative Adjectives

> **Articles:** **A** storm is predicted.
> Do you have **an** umbrella or **an** old raincoat?
> **The** rain should begin soon.
> **Demonstrative Adjectives:** **This** forecast is more accurate than **that** one.
> **These** reports are better than **those** reports.

A. Rewrite each sentence, using the correct word in parentheses.

1. (A, An) long time ago, there were no daily weather reports.

   _____

2. In (these, those) days, people couldn't predict weather as we can today.

   _____

3. That age was not as scientific as (this, that) one.

   _____

4. At (that, this) time, people depended more on natural signs.

   _____

5. Roosting birds were (a, an) indication of rain.

   _____

6. A red sky at night meant that (an, the) next day would be fair.

   _____

7. Red lightning meant that (a, an) storm was approaching.

   _____

8. In (those, these) days, weather prediction was less exact than now.

   _____

9. However, forecasters still use (these, those) signs of long ago.

   _____

10. (A, An) accurate forecast is the product of many different methods.

   _____

   (continued)

LANGUAGE AND USAGE

2 | **Articles and Demonstrative Adjectives** (continued from page 87)

B. Writing Application: Sentences

Write five sentences about natural changes that you might notice before a storm. Use articles and demonstrative adjectives in your sentences.

 Enrichment

Discover tomorrow's weather forecast. Color the spaces containing nouns that can be used with the article or the demonstrative adjective at the beginning of each row.

the	day	map	■	sea	snow	rain	■	wind	sky	ice
an	inn	sky	wind	eagle	day	age	map	ear	sea	clouds
a	city	icicle	eel	winter	ace	frost	egg	storm	ocean	uncle
this	time	night	cities	front	seas	spring	clouds	street	rivers	smog
these	clouds	wind	sea	hills	city	days	age	maps	log	charts
that	ocean	hills	clouds	wind	storms	snow	charts	heat	days	fall
those	days	moon	wind	clouds	tides	bees	sun	storms	charts	maps

Now write seven sentences about the weather. In each sentence, use a different article or demonstrative adjective and one of the nouns that you colored.

1. _____

2. _____

3. _____

4. _____

5. _____

6. _____

7. _____

LANGUAGE AND USAGE

3 | Comparing with Adjectives

Adjective	Comparing Two	Comparing Three or More
great	great**er**	great**est**
nice	nic**er**	nic**est**
easy	eas**ier**	eas**iest**
big	bi**gger**	bi**ggest**
important	**more** important	**most** important

A. Write the correct form of the adjective in parentheses to complete each sentence.

1. Mozart's story is one of the _____ in music. **(strange)**

2. He was one of the _____ composers in the world. **(young)**

3. He was _____ in music than in other subjects. **(interested)**

4. Few composers had _____ training than Mozart. **(thorough)**

5. His father was one of the _____ of all teachers. **(able)**

6. Mozart's performances were _____ than his composi-tions. **(popular)**

7. Yet he became the _____ composer of his time. **(brilliant)**

8. Mozart's works are among the _____ in music. **(beautiful)**

9. His operas are _____ than many other operas. **(funny)**

10. However, his music was _____ than his life. **(cheerful)**

11. Mozart was not the _____ person in the world. **(happy)**

12. Other musicians were _____ than he was. **(wealthy)**

13. Mozart's last days were the _____ days of all. **(sad)**

14. Mozart's brilliant career was _____ than others'. **(short)**

15. Yet his popularity is _____ now than ever before. **(great)**

16. He is one of the _____ composers of all time. **(fine)**

(continued)

LANGUAGE AND USAGE

3 | **Comparing with Adjectives** (continued from page 89)

B. Writing Application: Sentences

Write six sentences, comparing three songs that you know. Use an adjective that compares in each sentence.

★ Enrichment ★

Write an adjective beneath the first box in each row. Beneath the second box, write the form of the adjective that compares two. Beneath the third box, write the form of the adjective that compares three or more. Draw pictures to illustrate the three forms of the adjective. An example has been done for you.

ADJECTIVE	COMPARING TWO	COMPARING THREE OR MORE

1. ___difficult___	___more difficult___	___most difficult___

2. _____	_____	_____
		_____
3. _____	_____	_____

4. _____	_____	_____

Level 5 Unit 7 Adjectives   *(Use with pupil book pages 226–227.)*
Skill: Students will write the comparative and the superlative forms of adjectives.

LANGUAGE AND USAGE

4 | Comparing with *good* and *bad*

> *Good:* This is a **good** apple.
> This apple is **better** than that one.
> This is the **best** apple I've ever eaten.
>
> *Bad:* This looks like a **bad** pear.
> It looks **worse** than that pear.
> It looks like the **worst** pear in the bunch.

A. Complete each sentence by writing the correct form of *good.*

1. This is the _____ meal I have ever eaten.

2. Yes, Benita is a very _____ cook.

3. She is even _____ than I am.

4. She makes _____ stews than those the restaurant serves.

5. Her salads are very _____ too.

6. Her fruit salads are _____ than her vegetable salads.

7. The meat she serves is the _____ in town.

8. Her roast turkey is the _____ of all.

B. Complete each sentence by writing the correct form of *bad.*

9. The _____ meal I ever had here was a cheese sandwich.

10. Benita must have been in a very _____ mood.

11. The sandwich was _____ than the cafeteria's sandwiches.

12. It was even _____ than the meals at the diner.

13. It was the _____ sandwich in the world!

14. How can a cheese sandwich be that _____ ?

15. The bread tasted _____ than cardboard!

16. Actually, that part wasn't so _____ .

17. The _____ part of all was that there was no cheese!

18. A cheese sandwich without cheese is a pretty _____ sandwich.

(continued)

Level 5   Unit 7   Adjectives   *(Use with pupil book pages 228–229.)*
Skill: Students will use the correct forms of *good* and *bad.*

LANGUAGE AND USAGE

4 | **Comparing with *good* and *bad*** *(continued from page 91)*

C. Writing Application: Comparison and Contrast

Pretend that you have a job inspecting school cafeterias. Write a paragraph, comparing three meals that you have eaten in your school cafeteria. Use the adjectives *good, better, best, bad, worse,* and *worst* in your paragraph.

Enrichment

Henrietta reviews restaurants for a newspaper. You can help Henrietta write her next review. Think of a restaurant you know. Fill in the blanks labeled *adjective* with forms of *good* or *bad.* Follow the directions for filling in the other blanks.

_____ is a _____
   (name of restaurant)   (adjective)

restaurant. In fact, it is probably the _____
                                                              (adjective)

_____ restaurant outside _____ .
   (type of restaurant)   (name of country)

The _____ is _____ than
        (name of first dish)   (adjective)

that served in _____ . The _____
                        (name of city)   (name of second dish)

are the _____ I have ever eaten. Even
                  (adjective)

the _____ is _____ .
        (name of third dish)   (adjective)

_____ , with whom I am acquainted, is
        (name of chef)

a _____ chef. Recently, he was named
            (adjective)

the _____ chef in the country
          (adjective)

by _____ . It's amazing, but every year he
      (name of magazine)

gets _____ and _____ .
          (adjective)   (adjective)

LANGUAGE AND USAGE

5 | **Proper Adjectives**

Proper Nouns	Proper Adjectives
Africa	**African** fabrics
Greece	**Greek** olives
Central America	**Central American** food

A. Rewrite each sentence, using a proper adjective that is made from the proper noun in parentheses.

1. Bernardo saw __?__ linens at the world trade fair. **(Ireland)**

   _____

2. __?__ cameras were also on display. **(Japan)**

   _____

3. There was an exhibit of __?__ sculpture. **(North Africa)**

   _____

4. The __?__ sweaters looked warm. **(Scotland)**

   _____

5. The __?__ jade came in different shades of green. **(China)**

   _____

6. Bernardo gazed at the __?__ baskets. **(West Indies)**

   _____

7. He admired the __?__ carpets. **(Belgium)**

   _____

8. He sampled some __?__ foods. **(France)**

   _____

9. The __?__ machinery exhibit impressed him. **(Germany)**

   _____

10. The __?__ hosts had put on a good show. **(North America)**

    _____

(continued)

5 | **Proper Adjectives** *(continued from page 93)*

B. Writing Application: A List

You are a customs officer. Your job is to check the items that people bring into the United States from other countries. Make a list of ten items that you have checked. Use a different proper adjective to describe each item in your list.

Enrichment

Use the map to complete the sentences below. Write a proper adjective in each blank. You may use your dictionary.

1. Athens is the _____ capital.

2. Vienna is the _____ capital.

3. Prague is the _____ capital.

4. Warsaw is the _____ capital.

5. Lisbon is the _____ capital.

6. Bonn is the _____ capital.

7. Budapest is the _____ capital.

8. Copenhagen is the _____ capital.

9. Bucharest is the _____ capital.

COMPOSITION SKILL: DESCRIPTION

Using Sense Words

Sight:	blue, straight, tiny, brick
Sound:	silent, crashing, purring, roaring
Taste:	sweet, sour, tangy, bitter
Smell:	spicy, leathery, piny, soapy
Touch:	slippery, mushy, sharp, cool

Use your five senses to describe the items below. Write as many sense words as
you can to describe each item.

1. a skyscraper _____

_____

2. the wind against your face _____

_____

3. sand in your shoe _____

_____

4. a telephone _____

_____

5. an ambulance siren coming toward you _____

_____

6. rain clouds _____

_____

7. a frog _____

_____

8. the first day of spring _____

_____

9. the ocean _____

_____

10. a baby _____

_____

Level 5 Unit 8 Description   *(Use with pupil book pages 262–263.)*
Skill: Students will use sense words to describe how things look, sound, taste, smell, and feel.

COMPOSITION SKILL: DESCRIPTION

Using Exact Words

> **Without Exact Words:** My bike is pretty. It has some stuff.
> **With Exact Words:** My new bike is bright green. It has a rack and a tool kit.

Rewrite the following paragraphs. Replace the underlined words with vivid and exact words.

A.   Gilbert was sad. In the ten years since he was born, this was the worst birthday he had ever had. No one remembered. He even had to stay after school for some reason. He went home and opened the door. He heard a sound: "Surprise!" People were in the dining room. Lots of things were on the table. Gilbert was happy. "You really fooled me!" he said.

_____

_____

_____

_____

_____

_____

_____

B.   The chipmunk took a nut and put it in its mouth. Its mouth was so full that its cheeks stuck out. We laughed hard. The chipmunk looked at us. The chipmunk moved its tail and went away.

_____

_____

_____

_____

_____

Level 5 Unit 8 Description   *(Use with pupil book pages 263–264.)*
Skill: Students will rewrite paragraphs, using exact and vidid words.

COMPOSITION SKILL: DESCRIPTION

Choosing Details

> When you write a description, decide what impression you want to give your reader. Choose details to support your purpose.

Read the sentences below. Decide whether you want them to tell a happy story or a scary story. Then rewrite each sentence, adding at least two details that create an impression of happiness or fear.

1. Alonzo and I went for a walk one day.

   _____

2. We went to the woods.

   _____

3. We walked along a path.

   _____

4. After a while, we came to a cave.

   _____

5. There was a sign near it.

   _____

6. The opening was large.

   _____

7. Alonzo looked inside the cave.

   _____

8. I called out.

   _____

9. We went inside.

   _____

10. ''What a cave!'' Alonzo said.

   _____

COMPOSITION SKILL: DESCRIPTION

Organizing Your Description

Spatial order is one way to organize details in a description. Organize details from right to left, left to right, top to bottom, near to far, or far to near. Some spatial order words are *above, below, across, beside, opposite, inside, outside, next to, left,* and *right.*

You can also organize details in order of importance from the most to the least important or from the least to the most important. Some words that show the order of importance are *first, next, then, another,* and *finally.*

A. Write a list of five or six details describing your classroom. Organize your details from front to back. Use some words that tell the spatial order.

_____

_____

_____

_____

_____

_____

B. Write a list of five or six details describing your classroom. This time organize your details from least to most important.

_____

_____

_____

_____

_____

_____

THE WRITING PROCESS: DESCRIPTION

Step 3: Revise

Have I	yes
crossed out any details that do not support the purpose of the description?	☐
added sense words to describe how things look, smell, taste, sound, and feel?	☐
added exact words to help create a clear picture?	☐
changed the order of some sentences so that all the details are arranged in the same spatial order?	☐

Revise the following description. Use the check list above to help you. Check off each box when you have finished your revision.
- Use a thesaurus to help find exact words.
- Use the space above each line and on the sides of the paragraph for your changes.

This morning I took a walk in the first snow of the winter.

My boots made the first marks in the snow. The snow made noise

under my feet. I looked around. The air was cool and crisp against

my face. It seemed almost like spring. I could see my breath as I

breathed. At the next corner, snow-covered branches stretched

over the street. Just in front of me was a funny-looking heap of

snow. It was a car! The sky in the distance was gray. The sun was

covered by a haze. As I looked up, a few snowflakes fell

from the sky. I caught some on my tongue. They tasted fine. The

first snow had changed the way things looked.

Step 4: Proofread

proofread writing mistakes
always ~~proofread~~ your ~~writting~~ for ~~misteaks~~.

<table>
<tr><td colspan="2">Proofreading Marks</td></tr>
<tr><td>⊞</td><td>Indent.</td></tr>
<tr><td>∧</td><td>Add something.</td></tr>
<tr><td>𝒴</td><td>Take out something.</td></tr>
<tr><td>≡</td><td>Capitalize.</td></tr>
<tr><td>/</td><td>Make a small letter.</td></tr>
</table>

Proofread the following paragraph. Find four spelling errors, two capitalization errors, two punctuation errors, one run-on sentence, and one mistake in paragraph format. Find three errors in making comparisons with adjectives. Use proofreading marks to correct the errors. Use a dictionary to check your spelling.

Behind our home is a big apple tree. My Mother says that it was allready there before I was born. In the Winter the branches tap loudly against the howse. The wind blows loudly through the branches of the tree. I don't know whether the wind or the tree makes the loudest noise. The branches are covered with whight blossoms in the spring. When the apples get ripe, I climb on the branches there I have the most beautifulest view of the neighborhood. Then I shake the branches. Some apples fall out of the tree and I pick them up. I divide them into three groups. The perfect ones are for eating raw and the ones with broun spots are for cooking applesauce. The ones with worm holes are the worse of all. They are thrown away.

MECHANICS

 1 | **Capitalizing and Punctuating Sentences**

> **Declarative Sentence:**   **A** pentagon is a five-sided figure.
> **Imperative Sentence:**   **P**lease come to Washington**.**
> **Interrogative Sentence:** **I**s there a pentagon there**?**
> **Exclamatory Sentence:**   **I** can't wait to see it**!**

A. Write each sentence correctly. Separate any run-on sentences.

1. guess the size of the world's largest pentagon

_____

2. how big is it

_____

3. this five-sided figure measures about one mile around

_____

4. take a closer look at the Pentagon Building how huge it is

_____

5. it contains the United States Department of Defense

_____

6. what a huge department that is

_____

7. do you know that about 25,000 people work in the Pentagon

_____

8. that's a lot of people to feed does it have a large food service

_____

9. it has a bank and a post office it even has its own TV system

_____

10. go on a tour of the Pentagon tell me what you think of it

_____

(continued)

MECHANICS

1 | Capitalizing and Punctuating Sentences *(continued from page 101)*

B. Writing Application: A Description

You see a very strange building. What is unusual about it? Write six sentences, describing the building. Include a declarative sentence, an interrogative sentence, an imperative sentence, and an exclamatory sentence in your description.

★ Enrichment ★

The guide in the cartoons below is giving a tour of the Washington Monument. Write four captions, telling what is happening in these cartoons. Include a declarative sentence, an interrogative sentence, an imperative sentence, and an exclamatory sentence in your captions.

1.

_____

_____

3.
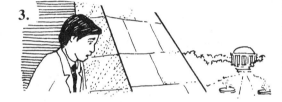

_____

_____

2.

_____

_____

4.

_____

_____

Now draw your own cartoon about a tour of a building you know. Write a caption beneath your cartoon.

MECHANICS

2 | Proper Nouns and Proper Adjectives

Proper Nouns:	Mexico	Taro Suzuki	Friday	Fourth of July
Proper Adjectives:	Mexican	Swiss	Greek	North American

A. Find the proper noun or proper adjective in each sentence. Write it correctly.

1. My friend linda mendez has a coin collection. _____

2. Some coins are from north african countries. _____

3. One egyptian coin is the size of a quarter. _____

4. A coin from the republic of china has a hole. _____

5. Recently she bought some ancient greek coins. _____

6. One has a picture of alexander the great. _____

7. Last monday she visited a coin exhibit. _____

8. She spent columbus day at a museum. _____

9. It was the metropolitan museum of art. _____

10. The museum featured coins during october. _____

11. There were displays of old roman coins. _____

12. Some had been found in the red sea. _____

13. A few came from ancient spanish ships. _____

14. The face of julius caesar decorated some. _____

15. Some showed portraits of caesar augustus. _____

16. Her trip to new york city was worth the effort. _____

17. Perhaps someday she will visit london. _____

18. The british museum has a good collection. _____

19. The victoria and albert museum also has one. _____

20. Some coin clubs tour the british isles. _____

(continued)

Level 5 Unit 9 Capitalization and Punctuation *(Use with pupil book pages 284–285.)*
Skill: Students will capitalize proper nouns and proper adjectives.

MECHANICS

2 | **Proper Nouns and Proper Adjectives**   *(continued from page 103)*

B. Writing Application: A Diary

Pretend that you are on a trip to a foreign country. Today you exchanged your money, toured a large city, and met a famous person. Write a diary entry, describing your day. Use at least three proper nouns and three proper adjectives.

★ Enrichment ★

You have been hired to design the money for a new country. Tell about the money by completing the sentences. Use a proper noun or a proper adjective in each answer.

1. The name of the country is _____ .

2. The money looks a little like _____ money.

3. The building you work in is called the _____ .

4. The person on one bill is named _____ .

5. That person is an important _____ citizen.

6. The person on another bill is named _____ .

Use the forms below to draw two of the bills that you designed. Include the information given in the sentences that you just completed.

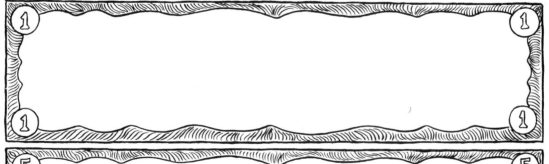

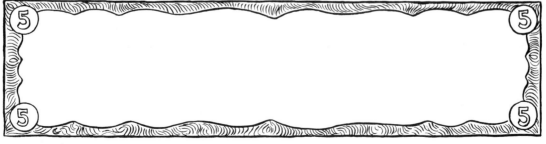

MECHANICS

3 | **Commas in a Series**

> My sister, my brother, and I watched the new family move in.
> We introduced ourselves, welcomed them, and invited them for dinner.

A. Rewrite each sentence that contains a series. Add commas where they are needed. For each sentence that does not include a series, write *none*.

1. Will Les Martha and Julie be going to our school?

   _____

2. Les will be in the same class as Alfredo and I.

   _____

3. His sisters are in the first third and fourth grades.

   _____

4. Let's invite them to play ball have a picnic swim or sunbathe.

   _____

5. We could meet them at the park in the school yard or at my house.

   _____

6. Let's wait until Thursday Friday or the weekend.

   _____

7. They just moved in and have a lot to do.

   _____

8. Right now they must unpack clean and move furniture.

   _____

B. Add commas to these sentences. Make the two sentences in each pair have different meanings.

9. Les James Martha May and Julie had a picnic in the park.

   Les James Martha May and Julie had a picnic in the park.

10. They ate cheese sandwiches tuna salad and eggs.

    They ate cheese sandwiches tuna salad and eggs.   *(continued)*

Level 5 Unit 9 Capitalization and Punctuation   *(Use with pupil book pages 286–287.)*
Skill: Students will use commas in a series.

MECHANICS

3 | **Commas in a Series** *(continued from page 105)*

C. Writing Application: A Newsletter

Pretend that you write a neighborhood newsletter. A new family has moved into your neighborhood. Write at least five sentences about who is in the family and what the neighbors are doing to welcome them. Use a series in each of your sentences.

Enrichment

Read the words written on the blackboard. Find words and phrases that can be grouped together. Write each group on the lines below.

history	pens	in the cafeteria	mathematics
interesting	in the library	rewarding	challenging
rulers	tuna sandwich	pencils	banana
applesauce	play chess	edit the	science
social studies	erasers	newspaper	
design a mural	milk	on the field	

1. _____   3. _____   5. _____

_____   _____   _____

_____   _____   _____

_____   _____   _____

2. _____   4. _____   6. _____

Now, on another piece of paper, write six sentences, telling new students about your school. Use each of the above groups of words in a series. Remember to use commas correctly.

MECHANICS

4 | More Uses for Commas

Introductory Words:	Oh, I heard about your class. Yes, it's great!
Nouns in Direct Address:	Elsa, come to my class with me.
	You will enjoy it, Elsa.
	You will see, Elsa, that it is useful.

A. Rewrite each sentence, adding commas where they are needed.

1. Yolanda I hear that you're taking a course in first aid.

   _____

2. Yes Willy I'm taking a course with Ms. Liang.

   _____

3. Can you tell me more about the course Yolanda?

   _____

4. Well Willy I've only had one class.

   _____

5. I wonder Yolanda if it's too late for me to sign up.

   _____

6. No I don't believe it is.

   _____

7. Why don't you come with me Willy?

   _____

8. Oh Ms. Liang let me introduce you to Willy.

   _____

9. Well you're just in time Willy to help with a demonstration.

   _____

10. Yolanda help me put Willy's arm in this sling.

    _____

(continued)

4 | **More Uses for Commas** *(continued from page 107)*

B. Writing Application: A Note

You know someone who is in the hospital. Write a note to wish that person a speedy recovery. Use the person's name at least three times in your note. Use the introductory words *oh, yes, well,* and *no* at least once. Remember to use commas correctly.

Enrichment

Study the cartoons below. Think of a story that will fit the pictures. Write what each character is saying. Use an introductory word or a noun in direct address in each speech balloon. Remember to use commas correctly.

Now draw your own cartoon on another piece of paper. Use an introductory word or a noun in direct address in each speech balloon.

Level 5 Unit 9 Capitalization and Punctuation   *(Use with pupil book pages 288–289.)*
Skill: Students will use introductory words and nouns in direct address in sentences.

MECHANICS

5 | Interjections

> **Hey!** Try to find some good seats.
> **Oh,** the balloon rally is starting!

A. Complete each line of this skit, using the interjection in parentheses. Use the correct punctuation after each interjection.

1. Safa: _____ The colors are fantastic!   **(Great)**

2. Lois: _____ That green one is the highest.   **(Wow)**

3. Willy: _____ what a beautiful sight!   **(Ah)**

4. Lois: _____ Hot-air ballooning might be fun.   **(Hey)**

5. Safa: _____ It's too early in the morning.   **(Good grief)**

6. Willy: _____ it's less windy in the morning.   **(Well)**

7. Safa: _____ a strong wind could be dangerous!   **(Oh)**

8. Lois: _____ Look at the tiny baskets!   **(Ha)**

9. Willy: _____ There are two people in each basket.   **(Goodness)**

10. Safa: _____ a larger balloon carries even more weight!   **(Well)**

11. Lois: _____ One balloon is descending early!   **(Oops)**

12. Willy: _____ It landed safely.   **(Whew)**

13. Safa: _____ guess who the first balloonists were!   **(Hey)**

14. Lois: _____ Is this a joke?   **(Oh, no)**

15. Safa: _____ a duck, a sheep, and a rooster were the first!   **(Ha)**

B. Writing Application: A Skit

    You and a friend are discussing a rubber raft trip that you have recently taken. Write a skit, using interjections to show feeling or emotion. Remember to use either an exclamation point or a comma after each interjection.   *(continued)*

Enrichment

The characters in the cartoon are hot-air ballooning. Tell what each character is saying about the view below them. Write a sentence in each speech balloon. Begin each one with an interjection. Use the correct punctuation after each interjection.

MECHANICS

6 Quotations

> The firefighter exclaimed, "Fire safety is important!"
> "You should know what to do in case of fire," she added.
> "There are rules," she explained, "that you should follow."
> "You must know some," she said. "Can you remember them?"

A. Rewrite each sentence, using punctuation marks and capital letters correctly.

1. the firefighter announced there are rules for fire safety

   _____

2. let's see if you know what they are she added

   _____

3. take care of flammable liquids said Tim keep them far from heat

   _____

4. should electrical wiring Mark asked be checked carefully

   _____

5. never overload an electrical outlet Judy exclaimed

   _____

6. Tim reminded don't stack newspapers, rags, or paints in basements.

   _____

7. plan escape routes suggested Judy in case of fire

   _____

8. have you ever held a fire drill in your home asked the firefighter

   _____

9. Mark exclaimed we certainly have

   _____

10. Tim sighed we should all check our homes more carefully

    _____

(continued)

MECHANICS

6 | Quotations *(continued from page 111)*

B. Writing Application: A Dialogue

You and a friend are having a conversation about fire safety. Your friend is asking you about safety precautions you take in your home, and you are answering. Write the dialogue, using direct quotations. Remember to use capital letters and punctuation marks correctly.

★ Enrichment ★

The students below drew posters to illustrate their reports on school fire drills. Use the posters to help you decide what each student is saying about fire safety. Then write a direct quotation for each picture.

1.

_____

_____

2.

_____

_____

3.

_____

_____

4.

_____

_____

5.

_____

_____

6.

_____

_____

Level 5 Unit 9 Capitalization and Punctuation   *(Use with pupil book pages 292–293.)*
Skill: Students will write direct quotations correctly.

MECHANICS

7 | Abbreviations

Titles:	Mister	**Mr.**	Junior	**Jr.**
	a married woman	**Mrs.**	Senior	**Sr.**
	any woman	**Ms.**	Doctor	**Dr.**
Businesses:	Corporation	**Corp.**	Limited	**Ltd.**
Days:	Tuesday	**Tues.**	Sunday	**Sun.**
Months:	February	**Feb.**	August	**Aug.**
Addresses:	Apartment	**Apt.**	Route	**Rte.**
States:	California	**CA**	Illinois	**IL**
Initials:	Susan Gloria	**S. G.**	Ling Chow	**L. C.**

A. Write these groups of words, using the correct abbreviations and initials.

1. Audio Service Corporation _____

2. Wednesday, September 29, 1875 _____

3. Alva John Holmes, Senior _____

4. Rodriguez, Incorporated _____

5. Friday, August 13, 1990 _____

B. Write these addresses. Use the correct abbreviations and initials for the under-lined words.

6. Doctor Jane Wilbur _____

   Route 30 _____

   Richmond, Virginia 23219 _____

7. Four Star Company, Limited _____

   Post Office Box 5555 _____

   Dallas, Texas 75234 _____

8. Mister Alonso Richard Amanda _____

   2001 Brentwood Avenue _____

   Springfield, Illinois 62704 _____

(continued)

MECHANICS

7 | Abbreviations *(continued from page 113)*

C. Writing Application: An Invitation

Write an invitation to invite your aunt to a school play. Include the date, the time of the play, and the address of your school. Use at least five abbreviations.

Enrichment

Use the code in the chart below to solve the puzzles. First, find the abbreviation for each state in the numbered list. Then write the letter the abbreviation stands for above the number of the state. The first one has been done for you.

CA	NY	TX	OR	IN	AL	DE	WA	VT	TN	ND	AK	IL
A	B	C	D	E	F	G	H	I	J	K	L	M
OH	**NM**	**GA**	**NE**	**FL**	**MI**	**CT**	**ME**	**CO**	**MO**	**SC**	**VA**	**KY**
N	O	P	Q	R	S	T	U	V	W	X	Y	Z

1. California
2. New York
3. New York
4. Florida
5. Indiana
6. Colorado

7. Vermont
8. California
9. Connecticut
10. Vermont
11. New Mexico
12. Ohio

13. Michigan
14. Texas
15. California
16. Ohio
17. New York
18. Indiana

19. Alabama
20. Maine
21. Ohio

A
‾ ‾ ‾ ‾ ‾ ‾ ‾ ‾ ‾ ‾ ‾ ‾ ‾
1 2 3 4 5 6 7 8 9 10 11 12 13

‾ ‾ ‾   ‾ ‾   ‾ ‾ ‾ !
14 15 16   17 18   19 20 21

Now solve this puzzle. Use the same code.

1. Virginia
2. New Mexico
3. Maine
4. California
5. Florida

6. Indiana
7. California
8. Texas
9. New Mexico
10. Oregon

11. Indiana
12. New York
13. Florida
14. Indiana
15. California

16. North Dakota
17. Indiana
18. Florida

‾ ‾ ‾   ‾ ‾ ‾
1 2 3   4 5 6

‾ ‾ ‾ ‾ ‾   ‾ ‾ ‾ ‾ ‾ ‾ ‾ !
7 8 9 10 11   12 13 14 15 16 17 18

Level 5   Unit 9   Capitalization and Punctuation   *(Use with pupil book pages 294–295.)*
Skill: Students will use abbreviations correctly.

MECHANICS

8 Titles

> I read the book **T**he **P**rince and the **P**auper.
> I read **T**he **D**aily **S**tar every morning.
> The chorus sang "**H**ome on the **R**ange."
> We read the poem "**T**he **S**ong of the **D**esert."

A. Write each sentence correctly.

1. Today's parktown crier, our newspaper, contained lots of information.

   _____

2. Joanna read a review of the book called the black stallion.

   _____

3. She is now reading the chapter called homeward bound.

   _____

4. Tod saw a review of the movie chariots of fire.

   _____

5. Now he's writing his own story, run for the gold.

   _____

6. Zelda read a report in the magazine called time.

   _____

7. She wanted to read an article called our changing language.

   _____

8. It contained the poem space rhymes.

   _____

9. Marco read about an old song called mr. tambourine man.

   _____

10. Then Marco wrote a song of his own called a banjo player.

   _____

(continued)

Level 5 Unit 9 **Capitalization and Punctuation**   *(Use with pupil book pages 296–297.)*
Skill: Students will capitalize and will punctuate titles.

MECHANICS

8 | **Titles** *(continued from page 115)*

B. Writing Application: A Letter

Your pen pal has asked you to recommend some books and movies. Write a letter to your pen pal, recommending your favorite book, short story, magazine, movie, poem, and song. Be sure to write the titles correctly.

★ Enrichment ★

You are the editor of your school newspaper. Below is a layout for the front page of the paper. Each block contains a brief description of a story. Write a name for the newspaper in the top space. Then think of a title for each story. Write the title above the description of the story.

VOL. XXIX   *   *   *   *   *   **MARCH 21, 1990**

_____   _____   _____

_____   _____   _____

a poem about   a short story about   an article about the
homework   a mountain-climbing   crowded conditions
                      expedition   in the cafeteria

_____   _____   _____

_____   _____   _____

a review of a new   a movie review   a book review
magazine for
teen-agers

Now, on another piece of paper, write a report to your teacher, telling about the subject of each article. Write six sentences. Include the title of a poem, a magazine, a short story, a movie, or a book in each sentence.

COMPOSITION SKILL: PERSUASIVE LETTER

Writing Business Letters

> A **business letter** is usually written for a purpose—to request information, order a product, apply for a job. Like a friendly letter, it has a heading, greeting, body, closing, and signature. It also has an *inside address*. When you write a business letter, use a colon *(:)* after the greeting. Close with *Sincerely* or *Yours truly*. Sign your full name.

A. Complete the business letter below. Address the letter to the Order Department. Request one copy of Birds of the Northeast that was advertised in the magazine Wildlife. Make up information to fill in any of the missing parts. Use the inside address given below.

Order Department
Wildlife, Inc.
P.O. Box 349
Los Angeles, CA 90004

_____

_____

_____

_____

_____

_____

_____

_____

_____

_____

_____

_____

(continued)

COMPOSITION SKILL: PERSUASIVE LETTER

Writing Business Letters *(continued from page 117)*

B. Write a business letter on the blanks below to Houghton Mifflin Company. Request a new catalogue of the books that the company publishes. Use your own address and today's date in the heading. Use the inside address below.

Houghton Mifflin Company
2 Park Street
Boston, MA 02108

_____

_____

_____

_____

_____

_____

_____

_____

_____

_____

_____

_____

_____

_____

_____

_____

_____

_____

_____

_____

Level 5 Unit 10 Persuasive Letter *(Use with pupil book pages 326–328.)*
Skill: Students will write a business letter, using the correct form.

COMPOSITION SKILL: PERSUASIVE LETTER

Stating and Supporting an Opinion

> State your opinion clearly and support it with strong reasons. To persuade others to accept your opinion, give reasons that will appeal to them.

Read the two opinion statements below. Then write four strong supporting reasons for each opinion. Use reasons that would appeal to an audience of your own age.

A. It is better to live in the country than in the city.

Reason 1: _____

_____

Reason 2: _____

_____

Reason 3: _____

_____

Reason 4: _____

_____

B. It is better to live in the city than in the country.

Reason 1: _____

_____

Reason 2: _____

_____

Reason 3: _____

_____

Reason 4: _____

_____

Ordering Your Reasons

Put reasons for an opinion in an order that will convince your audience, from *most* important to *least* important or from *least* important to *most* important.

Choose two of the topics listed below. Write a sentence for each one, stating an opinion about the topic. Then think of four reasons that can help you persuade your classmates to accept your opinion. Write your reasons on the blanks below in the order that you think will be most convincing to your audience.

gym for everyone every day	class party on the last day of school
lessons for emergency first aid	student art display in the front hall

A. Topic Sentence: _____

_____

Reasons: _____

_____

_____

_____

_____

_____

B. Topic Sentence: _____

_____

Reasons: _____

_____

_____

_____

_____

_____

THE WRITING PROCESS: PERSUASIVE LETTER

Step 3: Revise

Have I	yes
rewritten the topic sentence so that it clearly states the opinion?	☐
rewritten weak reasons to make them stronger and crossed out reasons that do not support the opinion?	☐
added reasons that will be convincing to the audience?	☐
arranged the reasons in order from most important to least important?	☐

Revise the following persuasive letter. Use the check list above to help you. Check off each box when you have finished your revision.

● Use the space above each line, on the sides, and below the letter for your changes.

Dear City Council Members:

Bike paths are a good idea. Don't you think that our

city should have them? More people would ride bicycles if they

had a safe place to ride them. Bike paths would be pretty too.

Flowers could be planted along the sides. There have been many

accidents between cars and bicycles in our city. People have

been badly hurt. I ride my bike to school, and I have to ride on

busy streets because there is nowhere else to ride. I hope that

you will consider my reasons and vote to build bike paths in our

city.

THE WRITING PROCESS: PERSUASIVE LETTER

Step 4: Proofread

Please send the *b*ooklet on a farmer's life, ~~wurk~~ *work*, and rewards.

Proofreading Marks	
⌐⌐	Indent.
∧	Add something.
℘	Take out something.
≡	Capitalize.
/	Make a small letter.

Proofread this business letter. Find three spelling errors, four capitalization errors, five punctuation errors, and one run-on sentence. Use proofreading marks to correct the errors. Use a dictionary to check your spelling.

4111 Spring garden Street

Phillipsburg NJ 08865

September 25 1990

To-A-Tee Shirt company

128 Ridge avenue

Norwalk, Ct 06854

Dear Sir or Madam

Our student counsel is lawnching a campaign to get more people to

vote.   We want to sell T-shirts saying VOTING IS FREE.   We'll sell

them to our parents, relatives and neibors will you make these shirts for

us?   If so, how much will they cost.

LANGUAGE AND USAGE

1 | Subject Pronouns

Nouns	**Subject Pronouns**
Manuel and Judy heard a speech.	**They** heard a speech.
The speaker was Mrs. Ruiz.	The speaker was **she**.

A. Write the subject pronoun that could replace the underlined word or words.

1. Manuel, Judy, and I have been reading about dinosaurs. _____

2. Dinosaurs became extinct millions of years ago. _____

3. The best-informed student is Manuel. _____

4. Judy and Manuel read about the brontosaur. _____

5. The brontosaur was one of the largest dinosaurs. _____

6. How large was this dinosaur? _____

7. Judy and I made a chart. _____

8. The chart gave a description of several dinosaurs. _____

9. The allosaurus and the stegosaur were included. _____

10. Judy showed the chart to Mrs. Ruiz and Mr. Li. _____

11. The science teacher is Mrs. Ruiz. _____

12. Mr. Li is an expert on dinosaurs. _____

13. A recent speaker at the science fair was Mr. Li. _____

14. The science fair was visited by several paleontologists. _____

15. Paleontologists are scientists who study fossils. _____

16. Fossils are prints found in rocks. _____

17. Judy and I learned a great deal from these scientists. _____

18. The person who was most impressed by the fair was Judy. _____

19. Next week Judy will visit the Museum of Natural History. _____

20. The museum has a wonderful display of dinosaur skeletons. _____

(continued)

Level 5 Unit 11 Pronouns *(Use with pupil book pages 346–347.)*
Skill: Students will use subject pronouns to replace nouns.

LANGUAGE AND USAGE

1 | **Subject Pronouns** *(continued from page 123)*

B. Writing Application: A Paragraph

You and your friends suddenly find yourselves living in the time of the dinosaurs. Write a paragraph about what you see. Use at least five subject pronouns in your paragraph. Underline each subject pronoun.

 Enrichment

Melissa Spencer and several other scientists have uncovered the skeleton of an enormous dinosaur. Melissa wants to telegraph her college to tell about her discovery. However, her message is too long. Rewrite the message, replacing nouns with subject pronouns. Make sure the message still makes sense.

WESTERN TELEGRAPH TELEGRAM

The other scientists and Melissa Spencer found the skeleton of a dinosaur STOP Melissa and the scientists think that the dinosaur weighed one hunded tons STOP The dinosaur was probably one hundred and twenty feet long STOP Several bones have already been uncovered STOP These bones still must be cleaned and identified STOP Melissa will be forwarding photographs of this discovery immediately STOP

Melissa Spencer

_____

_____

_____

_____

Now figure out the cost of the original telegram. There is a charge of $8.75 for the first ten words and $.45 for each additional word. Do not count the word *STOP* or Melissa's signature. Then figure out the cost of the rewritten telegram. How much money could Melissa have saved by using pronouns?

Original Telegram: _____ **Rewritten Telegram:** _____

Savings: _____

LANGUAGE AND USAGE

2 | Object Pronouns

Nouns	Object Pronouns
The Kents welcomed Fern.	The Kents welcomed **her**.
Fern went with the Kents.	Fern went with **them**.
Subject Pronoun	**Object Pronoun**
It was an interesting tour.	Fern liked **it**.

A. Rewrite these sentences, using the correct pronouns.

1. Mr. and Mrs. Kent gave Fern and (I, me) a tour of the bee farm.

_____

2. This was the first visit for (she, her) and (I, me).

_____

3. Mr. Kent told (we, us) that beekeepers are called apiculturists.

_____

4. (I, Me) asked (he, him) why beekeepers wear such strange clothing.

_____

5. The clothes protect (they, them) from bee stings.

_____

6. The Kents put beekeepers' veils on (we, us).

_____

7. (We, Us) followed (he, him) and (she, her) into the field.

_____

8. Mrs. Kent cautioned Fern and (I, me) to move slowly.

_____

9. (She, Her) explained to (we, us) that bees are social insects.

_____

10. (We, Us) watched (they, them) communicate by dancing.

_____

(continued)

2 | **Object Pronouns** *(continued from page 125)*

B. Writing Application: An Advertisement

You work in the advertising department of a book publishing company. Your assignment is to write an advertisement for a new book about bees. Tell why the book would be interesting to beekeepers, students, and scientists. Use subject and object pronouns in your advertisement. Underline the subject pronouns once and the object pronouns twice.

Enrichment

Mr. Kent has decided to post signs around the beehives, warning visitors about possible dangers. Help Mr. Kent by writing four warning sentences. Include at least one object pronoun in each warning.

1. WARNING!
   _____
   _____
   _____

3. WARNING!
   _____
   _____
   _____

2. WARNING!
   _____
   _____
   _____

4. WARNING!
   _____
   _____
   _____

LANGUAGE AND USAGE

3 | Using *I* and *me*

| Ella and **I** enjoy photography. | **I** enjoy photography. |
| Dad shows his photos to Ella and **me**. | Dad shows his photos to **me**. |

A. Rewrite each sentence, using the correct word or words in parentheses.

1. Ella and (I, me) went to a photography show.

   _____

2. It was an interesting experience for Ella and (I, me).

   _____

3. Dad decided not to go with Ella and (I, me).

   _____

4. He told (me and her, her and me) how to get to the show.

   _____

5. Ella and (I, me) took the bus.

   _____

6. The guide at the show spoke to Ella and (I, me).

   _____

7. Then she showed Ella and (I, me) the pictures.

   _____

8. (She and I, I and she) liked a picture of a sad woman.

   _____

9. The guide told (I, me) that it was called *Migrant Mother*.

   _____

10. Ella and (I, me) learned that the photographer was Dorothea Lange.

   _____

(continued)

Level 5 Unit 11 Pronouns   *(Use with pupil book pages 350–351.)*
Skill: Students will use *I* and *me* correctly.

LANGUAGE AND USAGE

3 | Using *I* and *me* *(continued from page 127)*

B. Writing Application: A Personal Narrative

Write about a trip you have taken with a friend. Write at least five sentences, telling where you went and what you saw. Use *I* or *me* in each sentence.

Enrichment

Underline the correct pronoun in parentheses to complete each riddle. Then write the answer to each riddle.

1. (I, Me) have holes on my sides. You put (I, me) in a camera. You need the camera and (I, me) to take photographs.

   I am _____ .

2. You can find my friends and (I, me) in museums. Sometimes (I, me) am black and white. Sometimes people take (I, me) with color film.

   I am a _____ .

3. Sometimes (I, me) am made of leather. (I, Me) have a strap. You can carry a camera in (I, me).

   I am a _____ .

4. Sometimes (I, me) am made of metal. (I, Me) have three legs. You use (I, me) to steady a camera.

   I am a _____ .

5. (I, Me) am made of paper. You can display photographs in (I, me). (I, Me) usually have a hard cover.

   I am a _____ .

6. (I, Me) am a place. There are no lights in (I, me). You can develop photographs in (I, me).

   I am a _____ .

Now, on another piece of paper, write two riddles of your own. Use the pronoun *I* or *me* in each sentence.

Level 5 Unit 11 Pronouns *(Use with pupil book pages 350–351.)*
Skill: Students will use *I* and *me* correctly.

LANGUAGE AND USAGE

4 | Possessive Pronouns

Before Nouns	Stand Alone
Her book is interesting.	The interesting book is **hers**.
My book is long.	**Mine** is long.

A. Rewrite each sentence, using the correct possessive pronoun in parentheses.

1. Today (our, ours) school is sponsoring a book fair.

   _____

2. Has (your, yours) ever had such an event?

   _____

3. (Our, ours) required a lot of preparation.

   _____

4. Actually (my, mine) teacher suggested the idea.

   _____

5. The idea of inviting famous authors was also (her, hers).

   _____

6. Peggy Parish and Steven Kellogg will talk about (their, theirs) works.

   _____

7. Peggy Parish will read from (her, hers) novel *Key to the Treasure*.

   _____

8. *Pirate Island Adventure* is also (her, hers).

   _____

9. After the fair, I will ask for (your, yours) comments.

   _____

10. Then I will give you (my, mine).

   _____

(continued)

Level 5 Unit 11 Pronouns *(Use with pupil book pages 352–353.)*
Skill: Students will choose possessive pronouns to complete sentences.

LANGUAGE AND USAGE

4 | **Possessive Pronouns** *(continued from page 129)*

B. Writing Application: Sentences

You and your friends are setting up a library for the younger children in your neighborhood. Write at least five sentences that tell what books you will have and who will donate the books. Use at least five different possessive pronouns.

 Enrichment

Find out what type of book each student enjoys reading. Use the clues below the chart to help you find the answers. Place an X under each category that you eliminate. Then draw a star in the box that shows what type of book each student likes best.

	Legend	Biography	Mystery	Science
Lee				
Bonnie				
Maria				
Seth				

CLUES

- No person's name begins with the same letter as his or her favorite type of book.
- Bonnie and Seth don't enjoy works of fiction.
- Lee and Maria don't like books that are nonfiction.

Now write a sentence that tells about each person's favorite type of book. Use a possessive pronoun in each sentence.

1. Lee: _____

2. Bonnie: _____

3. Maria: _____

4. Seth: _____

5. Bonnie and Seth: _____

6. Lee and Maria: _____

LANGUAGE AND USAGE

5 | Contractions with Pronouns

Pronoun + Verb	Contraction	Pronoun + Verb	Contraction
I am	I'm	we would	we'd
it is	it's	I have	I've
you are	you're	he has	he's
I will	I'll	you had	you'd

A. Write the contractions that can be made from the underlined words.

1. <u>I have</u> always liked big cats as much as Kim does. _____

2. <u>She is</u> reading about lions and tigers now. _____

3. <u>She has</u> purchased many posters of leopards and panthers. _____

4. <u>We are</u> going to see an exhibit about big cats. _____

5. <u>I am</u> impressed with their strength and grace. _____

6. <u>I will</u> take pictures of the exhibit. _____

7. You may come with us if <u>you would</u> like. _____

8. <u>It is</u> an interesting way to spend an afternoon. _____

9. The speaker will discuss the cats that <u>we have</u> read about. _____

10. <u>He will</u> tell about the spotted members of the cat family. _____

11. <u>They are</u> the most interesting to Kim. _____

12. <u>They have</u> adapted to their changing environment. _____

B. Write the pronoun and the verb that were combined to form the contraction in each sentence.

13. I'd go to Africa or Asia if I had the chance. _____

14. My friend Paul told me that he's been to Africa. _____

15. There you'll see lions in groups called prides. _____

16. It's easy to find tigers in some parts of Asia. _____

17. They'll be near water during the hot months. _____

18. You'd have a wonderful time in Asia and Africa. _____

(continued)

LANGUAGE AND USAGE

5 | Contractions with Pronouns *(continued from page 131)*

C. Writing Application: A Diary

You have been on a trip to Africa. While you were there, you photographed many wild animals. Write a diary entry about your adventures. Include at least five contractions that are made from pronouns and verbs.

Enrichment

Below are pictures that you took of big cats during a trip to Africa and Asia. Write a caption, telling what is happening in each picture. Each caption should be a complete sentence. The sentences can be humorous or factual. Use a different contraction in each sentence.

LIONS

1.

2.

_____ _____

LEOPARDS AND JAGUARS

3.

4.

_____ _____

TIGERS

5.

6.

_____ _____

LANGUAGE AND USAGE

6 | Double Subjects

> **Incorrect:** These **plants they** lived long ago.
> **Correct:**　 These **plants** lived long ago.
> 　　　　　　 **They** lived long ago.

A. Rewrite each sentence, correcting the double subject.

1. Poco and Marie they were collecting rocks for a science project.

   _____

2. Marie she found a piece of shiny black rock.

   _____

3. Poco he studied the piece carefully.

   _____

4. The rock it contained the print of a fern.

   _____

5. The print it is called a fossil.

   _____

6. Fossils they tell about the past.

   _____

7. Sometimes animal bones or shells they turn to stone.

   _____

8. This process it takes millions of years.

   _____

9. Poco he was impressed by Marie's discovery.

   _____

10. Later, Marie she showed the class the fossil.

    _____

(continued)

LANGUAGE AND USAGE

6 | **Double Subjects** (continued from page 133)

B. Writing Application: A Description

Imagine that you are a rock in the forest. You have been there thousands of years. Write a description of the people, the animals, or the plants that you have seen. Do not use any double subjects in your description.

Enrichment

A paleontologist, a scientist who studies fossils, is a kind of detective. You, too, can be a detective. Use the words on each fossil to make a sentence. There is one extra word on each fossil. Cross out that word. Then rewrite the correct sentence on the line.

1.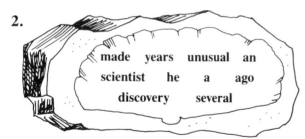

    like   somewhat   mammoths
    elephants   the   they   Asian
    and   African   looked

    _____
    _____
    _____

2.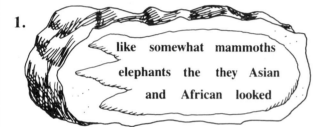

    made   years   unusual   an
    scientist   he   a   ago
    discovery   several

    _____
    _____
    _____

3.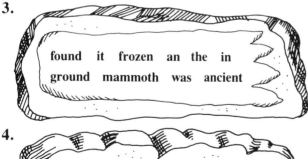

    found   it   frozen   an   the   in
    ground   mammoth   was   ancient

    _____
    _____
    _____

4.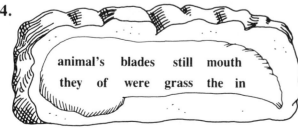

    animal's   blades   still   mouth
    they   of   were   grass   the   in

    _____
    _____
    _____

LANGUAGE AND USAGE

7 | Using *we* and *us* with Nouns

We students have a problem.   Those with no money are **we** children.
Dad gave **us** boys a lecture.   He often talks to **us** children about money.

A. Write *we* or *us* to complete each sentence correctly.

1. Sports equipment is expensive for _____ athletes.

2. _____ artists always seem to need paint supplies.

3. The biggest spenders are _____ students who are interested in fashion.

4. Obviously _____ spenders never have any money.

5. _____ children must earn some money.

6. Earning money does not come easily to _____ young people.

7. Bankers won't lend money to _____ children.

8. Those who have money will be _____ workers.

9. Selling plants is a possibility for _____ gardeners.

10. Neighbors will also give _____ students some business.

11. They will hire _____ gardeners to trim their lawns.

12. There are plenty of jobs for _____ fence painters.

13. Often _____ friends work together.

14. The children most often hired are _____ people who do odd jobs.

15. _____ delivery people can carry groceries and packages.

16. Drivers constantly hire _____ car washers.

17. The ones always in demand are _____ house cleaners.

18. There are many jobs for _____ baby sitters too.

19. Our parents will be proud of _____ workers.

20. Of course, those who will keep the most money are _____ savers!

(continued)

Level 5 Unit 11 Pronouns   *(Use with pupil book pages 358–359.)*
Skill: Students will use *we* and *us* correctly with nouns.

7 | Using *we* and *us* with Nouns *(continued from page 135)*

B. Writing Application: Sentences

Imagine that you and your classmates want to raise money to buy new sports equipment for your team. Write five sentences, telling what you and the other students will do to earn that money. In each sentence, use the pronoun *we* or *us* with a noun.

Enrichment

You and a group of your friends have decided to start your own companies. To attract customers, you will distribute fliers to your friends and neighbors. Describe your qualifications and the services you will provide. Write three sentences for each flier below. Use *we* or *us* with a noun in each sentence.

1. 🦴 DOG SITTING BY CARRIE AND HARRY 🦴

_____

_____

_____

2. (WASH + WAX $10) Andy and Randy's Car Wash (WASH $2)

_____

_____

_____

3. CUTTER'S LANDSCAPING SERVICE

_____

_____

_____

COMPOSITION SKILL: RESEARCH REPORT

Finding Facts

> A **dictionary** gives the spellings, pronunciations, and meanings of words.
> An **encyclopedia** gives basic information about many subjects.
> An **almanac** contains articles, lists, tables, and recent information.
> An **atlas** contains maps and tables that give information about places.
> **Newspapers** and **magazines** contain the most up-to-date information.
> **Nonfiction books** give facts about real people, places, and events.

Write *dictionary, encyclopedia, almanac, atlas, newspaper, magazine,* or *nonfiction book* to tell where you would look for the answer to each question.

1. What is the definition of the word *anthem*? _____

2. What is the title of the United States national anthem? _____

3. Who wrote the music for the United States national anthem?

   _____

4. What is the pronunciation of the word *anthem*? _____

5. Who fought in the War of 1812? _____

6. Where is Chesapeake Bay? _____

7. What happened in 1814 at Fort McHenry? _____

8. How many stars did the United States flag have when the national anthem was written? _____

9. How many verses does the United States national anthem contain?

   _____

10. Who was John Stafford Smith? _____

11. Who sang the anthem at yesterday's baseball game? _____

12. When was the United States national anthem adopted by Congress?

    _____

13. What is the world's oldest national anthem? _____

14. How does a songwriter go about writing the words for a song?

    _____

15. What is the national anthem of Great Britain? _____

COMPOSITION SKILL: RESEARCH REPORT

Taking Notes

Take notes to help you remember what you have read. Write down **key words** that will help you recall information. Include all important facts and use your own words.

Read the paragraph below. Then write notes to answer the question that follows.

Native North Americans had many ways of scaring crows away from their cornfields. Members of some tribes kept watch from platforms overlooking the cornfields. When a crow appeared, the people waved their arms and shouted until the bird flew off. Some Creek families lived close to their fields so that they could watch for crows and scare them away. Zuñi children made unusual scarecrows to place in their fields. The Zuñis also strung ropes throughout their cornfields. From the ropes, they hung bones and rags, which would blow in the wind. The sound and the sight of these items kept most birds away. The Navajos made scarecrows for their fields too. Sometimes they hung a dead crow from a stick, hoping that it would frighten other crows.

How did native North American farmers scare crows away from their cornfields?

_____

_____

_____

_____

_____

_____

_____

_____

_____

_____

Making an Outline

Make an outline from your notes by writing the questions as the **main topics**. Place each main topic after a Roman numeral and a period. List supporting facts as **subtopics**. Place each subtopic after a capital letter and a period. The first word of a main topic or subtopic starts with a capital letter. Give your outline a title.

Use the notes below to write an outline. Rewrite the questions as main topics and the notes that answer the questions as subtopics. Put the subtopics in an order that makes sense. Give your outline a title.

A. **What does a gray fox look like?**
—weighs seven to thirteen pounds
—salt-and-pepper coat with rust-colored legs
—tail about fourteen inches long
—head and body about twenty-five inches long
—bushy tail with black tip

Title: _____

_____

_____

_____

_____

_____

B. **What are the gray fox's habits?**
—hunts at night
—can climb trees to escape enemies
—lives in hollow logs, caves, or among rocks

_____

_____

_____

_____

COMPOSITION SKILL: RESEARCH REPORT

Writing a Paragraph from an Outline

Each section of an outline is about one main idea. When you write a paragraph from an outline section, think about the main idea to write a topic sentence for the paragraph. Write the subtopics as supporting details in complete sentences.

A. Write two good topic sentences for the outline section below. Place a check beside the topic sentence you prefer.

Great American Inventors

    I. Henry Ford (1863–1947)
        A. World-famous automobile maker
        B. Made first car in a shed behind home—1896
        C. Began the Ford Motor Company—1903
        D. Developed method of mass production
        E. Produced first inexpensive car—Model T

Topic Sentence: _____

_____

Topic Sentence: _____

_____

B. Now write a paragraph from the outline section above. Use the topic sentence you chose. Write supporting sentences based on the subtopics. Try to make your sentences interesting.

_____

_____

_____

_____

_____

_____

_____

_____

_____

_____

Level 5 Unit 12 **Research Report**   *(Use with pupil book pages 392–394.)*
Skill: Students will write topic sentences for an outline section and will write a paragraph from the outline section, using the topic sentence they prefer.

COMPOSITION SKILL: RESEARCH REPORT

Writing Openings and Closings

> Begin a report with an **introduction** that captures your reader's interest and tells what the report is about. End a report with a **conclusion** that sums up the main ideas.

A. Below are two possible openings and closings for a research report about the Loch Ness monster. Put a check beside the better opening and closing.

Openings:

_____ I don't think there is a Loch Ness monster.

_____ Beneath the calm surface of a lovely Scottish lake, a mysterious creature may be lurking.

Closings:

_____ Maybe I will try to catch Nessie someday!

_____ Thus, the mystery of the Loch Ness monster still remains to be solved.

B. Imagine that you wrote a report on icebergs from the following outline sections. Write two good openings and two good closings for the report. Then put a check beside the opening and closing you think are better.

Icebergs

    I. Description of iceberg
        A. Mountain of ice floating in ocean
        B. Piece broken off glacier (huge field of ice)
        C. In summer, floats south from Arctic to Canada
    II. Size of iceberg
        A. Most of iceberg under water
        B. May be 400 feet above water
        C. Can be many miles long

Opening: _____

_____

Opening: _____

_____

Closing: _____

_____

Closing: _____

_____

Level 5 Unit 12 Research Report *(Use with pupil book pages 394–395.)*
Skill: Students will choose the better of two openings and closings for a report and will write two openings and closings for a report on a given topic.

THE WRITING PROCESS: RESEARCH REPORT

Step 4: Revise

Have I	yes
replaced the weak opening with an interesting one?	☐
written a topic sentence for the paragraph?	☐
combined facts to make a sentence more interesting and moved one fact so that the order makes sense?	☐
replaced unclear pronouns and added details to make a sentence clearer?	☐

Revise the following paragraph from a research report. Use the check list above to help you. Check off each box when you have finished your revision.

• Use the space above each line, on the sides, and below the paragraph for your changes.

• Use the outline section below to write a topic sentence and to check that all the facts have been used in the paragraph.

    I. Methods of voting
        A. All must register
        B. All voting secret
        C. Paper ballots dropped into locked box
        D. Voting machines—voter moves pointer to cast vote
        E. Some machines computerized
        F. Absentee ballots for voters who are ill or out of town

    This report is about voting. They must be registered. One method is to mark a paper ballot and drop it into a locked box. All voting is secret. Another method is to use a voting machine. They move pointers on the machines to cast their votes. Some of them are computerized. Voters can use absentee ballots.

Step 5: Proofread

does quills
~~why do~~ a Porcupine have ~~quills~~ ?

Proofreading Marks	
⊓	Indent.
∧	Add something.
ℓ	Take out something.
≡	Capitalize.
/	Make a small letter.

Proofread the following report. There are three spelling errors, four capitalization errors, and one mistake in paragraph format. There are two punctuation errors and two run-on sentences. There are three mistakes in the use of pronouns. Use proofreading marks to correct the errors. Use a dictionary to check your spelling.

the Porcupine

Have you ever met a porcupine. I have. These prickly animals are dark brown,

and them have long, stiff quills on their backs, sides, and tails Most people think

that porcupines shoot their quills, this, however, is not true. the quills just have a

way of comeing out easily when the animal is attacked. The quills can cause

serious problems for animals who are stuck by it.

Only one kind of porcupine lives in north America. They can be found mainly

in pine Forests. It eats tree bark and plants it may kill a tree by takeing off the

bark in this way. In the spring, the female porcupine gives birth to a single baby.

Surprisingly enuf, the babies have quills when they are born.

LANGUAGE AND USAGE

 Adverbs

> **How:** The artist painted **carefully**.
>
> **When:** **Soon** she displayed her work.
>
> **Where:** Her paintings hung **there**.

A. Underline the adverb in each sentence. Then write whether the adverb tells *how, when,* or *where.*

1. Anna Mary Robertson always helped her mother. _____

2. She patiently took care of the younger children. _____

3. Then she became a housekeeper. _____

4. Her employers lived nearby. _____

5. A hired man worked there with her. _____

B. Write the adverb in each sentence. Then draw an arrow from the adverb in the sentence to the verb that it describes.

6. Eventually Anna Mary married the man, Thomas Moses. _____

7. Anna and Tom worked hard. _____

8. They successfully ran a dairy business. _____

9. Later Anna began painting. _____

10. The eighty-year-old artist worked inside. _____

11. Her bedroom studio was upstairs. _____

12. Anna remembered her childhood vividly. _____

13. She skillfully used a primitive style of painting. _____

14. Her paintings sold well. _____

15. Soon critics referred to her as Grandma Moses. _____

16. Exhibitors displayed her paintings everywhere. _____

(continued)

Level 5 Unit 13 Adverbs and Prepositions *(Use with pupil book pages 412–413.)*
Skill: Students will identify adverbs and the verbs that they modify.

LANGUAGE AND USAGE

1 | **Adverbs** *(continued from page 145)*

C. Writing Application: A Paragraph

Think of something that you do well. Your special talent could be in art, in sports, in science, or in some other field. Write a paragraph about your special talent. Use adverbs that tell how, when, and where.

Enrichment

Artists use colors when they paint pictures, but writers use words. You can use describing words, such as adverbs, to "paint a picture" or to create an image. The adverbs you choose make the picture clearer. On the paint cans below, list adverbs that tell how, when, and where.

HOW
carefully

WHEN
yesterday

WHERE
indoors

Now use these adverbs to write five different sentences. For each sentence, add two different adverbs to the short sentence below. Notice how the meaning of each sentence and the picture you have created change when you use different adverbs.

| The artist painted. |

Example: **Yesterday** the artist painted **indoors.**

1. _____

2. _____

3. _____

4. _____

5. _____

Level 5 Unit 13 Adverbs and Prepositions   *(Use with pupil book pages 412–413.)*
Skill: Students will use adverbs in sentences.

LANGUAGE AND USAGE

2 | Comparing with Adverbs

Adverb	Comparing Two	Comparing Three or More
close	clos**er**	clos**est**
early	earl**ier**	earl**iest**
swiftly	**more** swiftly	**most** swiftly

A. Write the correct form of the adverb in parentheses to complete each sentence.

1. Tala lives _____ to school than Ali does. **(close)**

2. She arrived at the auditorium _____ than Ali did. **(early)**

3. Ali arrived _____ of all the students. **(late)**

4. The final speaker spoke _____ than the others. **(long)**

5. She talked _____ than the first speaker. **(excitedly)**

6. She spoke _____ of all about monkeys and apes. **(earnestly)**

7. Chimpanzees resemble gorillas _____ of all the apes. **(closely)**

8. Do gorillas scream _____ than other apes do? **(loud)**

9. Chimpanzees learn _____ of all the apes. **(quickly)**

10. A gibbon moves _____ than a monkey does. **(fast)**

11. The gibbon can climb _____ than a gorilla can. **(high)**

12. Spider monkeys climb _____ of all the monkeys. **(gracefully)**

13. Gibbons move _____ on land than in the trees. **(clumsily)**

14. Of all these apes, chimpanzees behave _____ . **(peacefully)**

15. A baboon fights _____ than a gorilla does. **(often)**

16. Gorillas try _____ of all apes to avoid fights. **(hard)**

17. Rhesus monkeys act _____ of all monkeys. **(fiercely)**

18. Of all the apes, chimps act _____ to humans. **(friendly)**

(continued)

LANGUAGE AND USAGE

2 | Comparing with Adverbs *(continued from page 147)*

B. Writing Application: Comparison and Contrast

Pretend that you are a zoo keeper. Write a comparison of some of the animals in your zoo. Compare and contrast the habits and personalities of at least three of the animals. Include an adverb that compares in each sentence.

Enrichment

Read the chart to discover some interesting facts about certain kinds of animals. Then write adverbs that compare to complete the sentences below.

ANIMALS THAT JUMP HIGH	thoroughbred horse	8 feet	puma	23 feet
	hare	7 feet	impala	10 feet
	cat	6 feet	tiger	13 feet
ANIMALS THAT HAVE A LONG LIFE SPAN	Madagascar tortoise	200 years	chimpanzee	51 years
	Asian elephant	69 years	raven	69 years
	Pearl mussel	100 years	lobster	50 years
ANIMALS THAT RUN FAST	cheetah	71 mph	zebra	40 mph
	giraffe	31 mph	lion	50 mph
	camel	10 mph	hare	45 mph
ANIMALS THAT MOVE SLOWLY	garden snail	17 feet per hour		
	sloth	5 feet per hour		
	red slug	6 feet per hour		

1. Of all the animals, the cheetah runs _____ .

2. Of all the animals, the sloth moves _____ .

3. The hare can jump _____ than the cat.

4. Of all the animals, the Madagascar tortoise lives _____ .

5. The zebra moves _____ than the hare.

6. Of all the animals, the puma can jump _____ .

7. The Asian elephant lives _____ than the chimpanzee.

8. The red slug moves _____ than the sloth.

Now use the information in the chart to write two sentences of your own. Compare the actions of two or more animals in each sentence.

9. _____

10. _____

LANGUAGE AND USAGE

3 | Adjective or Adverb?

Adjectives	Adverbs
Jeanette Rankin was **confident**.	She spoke **confidently**.
She felt **well**.	She expressed herself **well**.
She did a **good** job.	She did her job **well**.

A. Underline the correct word in parentheses to complete each sentence. Then write *adjective* or *adverb* for each underlined word.

1. April 6, 1917, was (special, specially). _____

2. Would the important vote in Congress go (good, well)? _____

3. Most politicians supported the war (firm, firmly). _____

4. Their speeches that day were (good, well). _____

5. Jeanette Rankin thought war was (wrong, wrongly). _____

6. She believed (strong, strongly) in peace. _____

7. That morning Jeanette did not feel (good, well). _____

8. She rose to her feet (slow, slowly). _____

9. She expressed her opinion (good, well). _____

10. The first woman in Congress spoke (clear, clearly). _____

11. Her vote against the war was (definite, definitely). _____

12. The Speaker of the House was (angry, angrily). _____

13. The votes were counted (quick, quickly). _____

14. Jeanette's side lost (bad, badly). _____

15. Her decision had been (difficult, difficultly). _____

16. Jeanette (sure, surely) had offended many people. _____

17. Most people did not treat her (good, well). _____

18. Later, people remembered her courage (good, well). _____

(continued)

LANGUAGE AND USAGE

3 | **Adjective or Adverb?**   *(continued from page 149)*

B. Writing Application: A Biography

Write a short biography of a famous person or of someone you know who performed a courageous act or took an unpopular stand. Use three adjectives and three adverbs in your biography. Include *good* and *well*. Underline each adjective. Circle each adverb.

Enrichment

The last names of some courageous people are hidden in the sentences below. Circle each last name, and write the full name on the line. Then complete each pair of sentences. Write an adjective to complete the first sentence. Then complete the second sentence with an adverb that is made by adding *-ly* to the adjective.

Example: Rosa was tired from walking all the way from the(park, so she sat in the

first seat she could find on the bus. _____**Rosa Parks**_____

Rosa was ___courageous___ . She worked ___courageously___ for civil rights.

1. Paul warned the minutemen and forever enjoyed the respect of the colonists.

    _____

    The night was _____ . He shouted _____ .

2. Florence strode out at night in gales and rain to help the wounded soldiers.

    _____

    Her lamp was _____ . It shone _____ in the night.

3. As Harriet waited for the signal, the slave was forced to hide behind the

    bathtub many hours. _____

    Harriet was _____ . She fought _____ for freedom.

4. Neil held in his arm strong evidence that the United States was the first to land

    a person on the moon. _____

    Neil was _____ . He stood _____ on the lunar surface.

LANGUAGE AND USAGE

 Negatives

> Incorrect: I **haven't never** used a computer.
> Correct: I **have never** used a computer.
>   I **haven't ever** used a computer.

A. Rewrite each sentence, correcting the double negative.

1. I never used nothing so difficult.

   _____

2. Doesn't nobody know how to work this computer?

   _____

3. I don't see no directions anywhere.

   _____

4. Won't nobody help me?

   _____

5. I still don't see nothing on the screen.

   _____

6. No one never plugged in the computer.

   _____

7. I don't see the plug nowhere.

   _____

8. Don't none of these computer disks work?

   _____

9. Isn't there no one we can call for help?

   _____

10. Won't this computer never work?

   _____

(continued)

Level 5   Unit 13   Adverbs and Prepositions   *(Use with pupil book pages 418–419.)*
Skill: Students will correct double negatives.

LANGUAGE AND USAGE

4 | **Negatives** *(continued from page 151)*

B. Writing Application: An Advertisement

Pretend that you work for an advertising company. You must write an advertisement for a new computer. Use a negative in each sentence of your advertisement. Be sure that you do not use any double negatives.

★ Enrichment ★

Computer information is usually stored on small, flat disks. These disks are very sensitive and require special handling. The warning signs below show the things we should not do when we are working with computer disks. Write a sentence for each warning sign. Use one negative word in each sentence.

1.

_____

_____

_____

3.

_____

_____

_____

2.

_____

_____

_____

4.

_____

_____

_____

5 | Prerositions

> preposition object
> The architect displayed the drawing **of** the house.
>
> preposition object
> She showed it **to** them.

A. Underline the preposition in each sentence. Then write the object of the preposition.

1. Harriet designs buildings of many types. _____

2. She is working on several projects. _____

3. Her office is inside this building. _____

4. Blueprints are scattered across her desk. _____

5. Her drafting table is under a skylight. _____

6. A detailed model is by the window. _____

7. Several miniature trees are around it. _____

8. Harriet spends long hours in this office. _____

9. However, she also goes to the construction site. _____

10. She brings the blueprints with her. _____

11. A supervisor meets her at the gate. _____

12. Harriet walks through the structure. _____

13. She checks below the ground level. _____

14. She climbs up the ladder. _____

15. The workers talk about the project. _____

16. Problems are discussed during this meeting. _____

17. These problems cannot wait until the last minute. _____

18. The architect must find solutions for them. _____

(continued)

LANGUAGE AND USAGE

5 | Prepositions *(continued from page 153)*

B. Writing Application: A Persuasive Letter

A new community center is being planned for your town. As an architect, you would like to design the building. Write a persuasive letter to the building committee, telling why you think your design is best. Include at least five prepositions in your letter. Underline the prepositions.

Enrichment

Below is an architect's plan for a new house. The new owners, Mr. and Mrs. Lang, want to see where their furniture will fit. You can help them with the arrangement by drawing the furniture where you think it should be placed. Use the symbols shown below for the furniture.

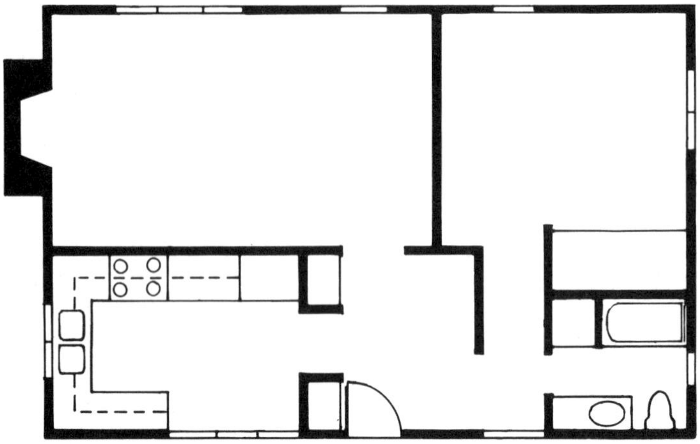

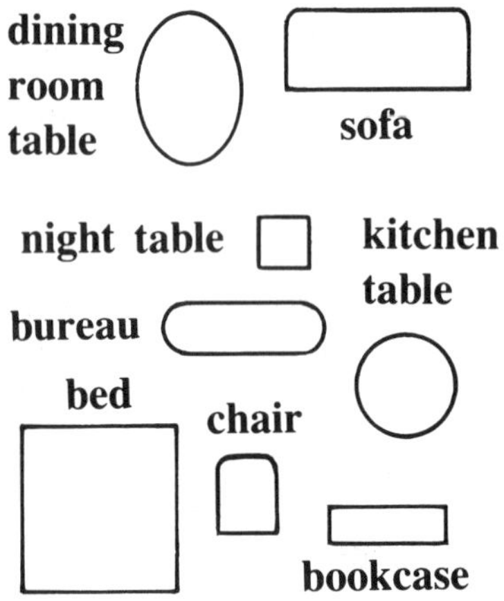

dining room table

sofa

night table   kitchen table

bureau

bed   chair

bookcase

Now write a paragraph, describing your suggestions for the placement of the furniture. Use a preposition in each sentence. Underline each preposition once and the object of the preposition twice.

_____

_____

_____

_____

_____

_____

LANGUAGE AND USAGE

 Prepositional Phrases

> preposition object   object
> Mistakes **in construction** and **manufacturing** can be dangerous.
>   prepositional phrase
>
>   preposition   object
>   Laws protect people **from** these **mistakes**.
>   prepositional phrase

A. Write the prepositional phrase in each sentence. Underline the preposition once and the object of the preposition twice.

1. The Tacoma Narrows Bridge in Washington opened forty-five years ago.

   _____

2. The bridge was built across Puget Sound. _____

3. At that time, it was the world's third largest suspension bridge.

   _____

4. Soon passengers inside cars and buses noticed that the bridge swayed.

   _____

5. After a few weeks, people began calling the bridge Galloping Gertie.

   _____

6. Crossing the bridge resembled a ride on a roller coaster or a boat.

   _____

7. During strong winds, the bridge swayed violently.

   _____

8. Officials finally closed the bridge to vehicles and people.

   _____

9. Eventually the deck fell into the water. _____

10. Now models of bridges must first be tested.

    _____

(continued)

Level 5 Unit 13 Adverbs and Prepositions   *(Use with pupil book pages 422–423.)*
Skill: Students will identify prepositional phrases, prepositions, and the objects of prepositions.

LANGUAGE AND USAGE

6 | **Prepositional Phrases** *(continued from page 155)*

B. Writing Application: A Description

Think of an exciting or unusual trip that you have taken. Write a paragraph, describing that trip. Use at least five prepositional phrases in your description. Underline each prepositional phrase.

Enrichment

Below is a map of the town of Shambletown, which is in the state of Disrepair. Buster is anxious to get to the Fix-It Shop. Draw the route he should follow. He may not cross any broken bridges.

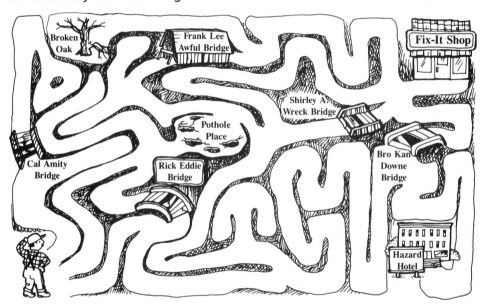

Now write directions, telling Buster how to reach the Fix-It Shop. Use a prepositional phrase in each sentence of your directions.

_____

_____

_____

_____

_____

_____

LANGUAGE AND USAGE

7 | Object Pronouns in Prepositional Phrases

> The exercise teacher ran past **me**.
> I jogged after the other **students** and **him**.

A. Rewrite each sentence, using the correct pronoun in parentheses. Then underline the prepositional phrase in the sentence that you wrote.

1. Exercise classes are held near (us, we).

   _____

2. Ms. Jay and Mr. Petrie usually arrive before my parents and (I, me).

   _____

3. From (her, she) and (him, he), we learn different exercises.

   _____

4. We always do warm-up exercises with the other students and (them, they).

   _____

5. Ms. Jay explains the exercises to (we, us).

   _____

6. No one except Mom and (I, me) can do sit-ups.

   _____

7. The student beside Dad and (her, she) couldn't do pushups.

   _____

8. One beginner behind Mom and (he, him) thinks that leg lifts are easy.

   _____

9. For my parents and (I, me), these exercise classes are fun.

   _____

10. Without (they, them) we wouldn't stay fit.

   _____

(continued)

LANGUAGE AND USAGE

7 | Object Pronouns in Prepositional Phrases (continued from page 157)

B. Writing Application: A List

Think of an activity that you and other students do in gym class. Write a list of sentences, explaining the steps involved in this activity. In each sentence, use a prepositional phrase with an object pronoun. Underline the prepositional phrases.

Enrichment

Read the first sentence in each pair below. Then write a prepositional phrase to complete the second sentence. The phrases you write are parts of common expressions. Each prepositional phrase should consist of a preposition and at least one pronoun.

1. Bo and Mo will learn crossovers. Just keep _____ .

2. He just did one hundred pushups! I can't get _____ !

3. Millicent just can't do knee bends. Stop picking _____ .

4. Zeke and Joe are having trouble. Can we cover _____ ?

5. Si and Sophie need our support. Let's all get _____ .

6. Sophie doesn't know her own ability. In fact, she runs rings

    _____ in weightlifting.

7. Sophie loves weightlifting. She's nuts _____ .

8. Nella and I are learning to do leg lifts. Try to bear _____ .

9. We know that the team can do better. Let's build a fire _____ .

10. Mac tried to do fewer sit-ups, but he didn't get away _____ .

11. Zoe and Mac think these classes are difficult. The classes are beginning to

    get _____ .

12. Ava and he don't listen to the instructions. The teachers find it difficult to get

    through _____ .

LANGUAGE AND USAGE

8 | Adverb or Preposition?

> **Adverb:** The drawbridge moved **down**.
>
> **Preposition:** The knight rode **down** the path.

A. If the sentence has an adverb, write the adverb. If it has a prepositional phrase, underline the prepositional phrase and write the preposition.

1. Several tourists mingled outside.   _____

2. More visitors waited inside.   _____

3. Hilary walked up the stairs.   _____

4. A knight in armor guarded the entrance.   _____

5. He put his helmet down.   _____

6. She passed by.   _____

7. She peered inside the darkened room.   _____

8. A guide invited her in.   _____

9. Hilary strolled around.   _____

10. Armor was displayed along all the walls.   _____

11. Hilary read the explanation above the armor.   _____

12. She looked up.   _____

13. Decorated shields dangled above.   _____

14. Heavy metal helmets hung below the shields.   _____

15. Hilary looked down a long hallway.   _____

16. Near the end was a jewel display.   _____

17. Hilary walked by the display.   _____

18. Shields had glittering jewels around their edges.   _____

(continued)

Level 5   Unit 13   **Adverbs and Prepositions**   *(Use with pupil book pages 426–427.)*
Skill: Students will identify and will distinguish between adverbs and prepositions.

LANGUAGE AND USAGE

8 | **Adverb or Preposition?**   *(continued from page 159)*

B. Writing Application: A Speech

Pretend that you are a museum guide in the year 2525. You are taking a group of students around a display of twentieth-century machines. Write a short speech, describing where you are walking and what is on exhibit in the museum. Use at least three adverbs and three prepositions in your speech.

Enrichment

Imagine that you are a tour guide at an ancient castle. Each day you answer many questions from visitors. Using the picture below, write a sentence to answer each of the following questions. Use a word from the box in each sentence. Write your sentences on another piece of paper.

around	outside	over	up	down
inside	below	above	near	under

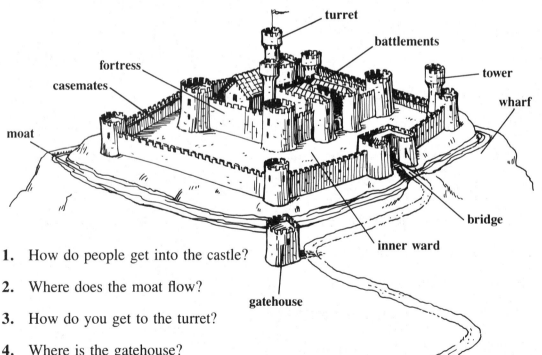

1. How do people get into the castle?

2. Where does the moat flow?

3. How do you get to the turret?

4. Where is the gatehouse?

5. Where is the fortress?

6. Can you see the moat from the tower?

Level 5   Unit 13   Adverbs and Prepositions   *(Use with pupil book pages 426–427.)*
Skill: Students will identify adverbs and prepositions in sentences.

Teacher's Annotated Pages

What Is a Sentence?

Sentences: Band music is very popular with people of all ages.
People have listened to bands for hundreds of years.

Sentence Fragments: Band music.
Is very popular with people of all ages.
For hundreds of years.

A. Write *S* after each group of words that is a sentence. Write *F* after each group of words that is a sentence fragment.

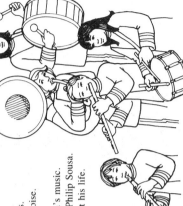

1. John Philip Sousa was a famous bandleader. __S__
   From 1854 to 1932. __F__

2. Sousa was born in Washington, D.C. __S__
   Visited many places around the world. __F__

3. More than one hundred marches. __F__
   Sousa wrote music. __S__

4. You probably know some of his music. __S__
   "The Stars and Stripes Forever." __F__

5. Can listen to his records in school. __F__
   You can buy records of Sousa's marches. __S__

B. Change each fragment above into a complete sentence. Sample answers:

6. He lived from 1854 to 1932.
7. He visited many places around the world.
8. Sousa wrote more than one hundred marches.
9. "The Stars and Stripes Forever" is played often.
10. We can listen to his records in school.

(continued)

What Is a Sentence?   (continued from page 1)

C. **Writing Application: A Music Review**

Think about a record that you like. Write five sentences telling why you like it. Make sure that your sentences are complete.
Students to respond on separate paper. Answers will vary.

★ Enrichment ★

Find the five complete sentences below. Write the sentences in order on the lines. Then circle the first letter of each sentence. The letters you circle will spell the name of something that is important in a band.

1. Several kinds of bands.
2. Dance bands are popular.
3. On records or on tape.
4. Radios play band music.
5. Once in a while a loud noise.
6. Playing in a band.
7. Many students like Sousa's music.
8. Trying to play like John Philip Sousa.
9. Sousa wrote a book about his life.

(Ⓓ)ance bands are popular. _____
(Ⓡ)adios play band music. _____
(Ⓤ)sually people like bands. _____
(Ⓜ)any students like Sousa's music. _____
(Ⓢ)ousa wrote a book about his life. _____

Name _____

LANGUAGE AND USAGE   WORKBOOK PLUS ▲ 4

2 | Four Kinds of Sentences (continued from page 3)

B. Writing Application: A Message

You have been shipwrecked on an island in the middle of the ocean. You find a piece of paper, a pencil, and a bottle. Write a message to put into the bottle. Your message must include one declarative sentence, one interrogative sentence, one imperative sentence, and one exclamatory sentence.

Students to respond on separate paper. Answers will vary.

Enrichment

The students in Mr. Novak's class wanted to make the invitations to their party sound like telegrams. Instead of using end punctuation, they ended every sentence with the word *STOP*. Rewrite the invitation on the lines below. Replace each *STOP* with the correct end punctuation.

TELEGRAM

We are having a party Thursday afternoon STOP Can you come STOP It will be such fun STOP Bring this invitation with you STOP Present it at the door STOP

Mr. Novak's class

TELEGRAM

We are having a party Thursday afternoon. Can you come? It will be such fun! Bring this invitation with you. Present it at the door.

Now underline the first word in each imperative sentence you have written. The words form a hidden message. Write the message here.

Bring present.

Level 5 Unit 1 The Sentence   (Use with pupil book pages 16–17.)
Skill: Students will write and will punctuate the four kinds of sentences.

Name _____

LANGUAGE AND USAGE   WORKBOOK PLUS ▲ 3

2 | Four Kinds of Sentences

Declarative Sentence: There are many ways of sending messages.
Interrogative Sentence: How many ways do you know?
Imperative Sentence: Take this note to your mother.
Exclamatory Sentence: What a strange message this is!

A. Write the correct end punctuation for each sentence. Then label each sentence *declarative, interrogative, imperative,* or *exclamatory.*

1. Have you ever received a telegram ? _interrogative_
2. How exciting it is ! _exclamatory_
3. Telegrams were popular before we had telephones . _declarative_
4. Do you know who invented the telegraph ? _interrogative_
5. Read about it here . _imperative_
6. Samuel F. B. Morse was one of the inventors . _declarative_
7. What a clever person he was ! _exclamatory_
8. He also invented Morse code . _declarative_
9. Do you know how to use Morse code ? _interrogative_
10. Learn to use Morse code . _imperative_
11. Have you heard that Morse was also an artist ? _interrogative_
12. What wonderful portraits he painted ! _exclamatory_
13. Have you seen any of his paintings ? _interrogative_
14. Some of his work is displayed in New York . _declarative_
15. Please try to find out more about Morse . _imperative_
16. Look up his name in the encyclopedia . _imperative_
17. What interesting facts you will discover ! _exclamatory_

(continued)

Level 5 Unit 1 The Sentence   (Use with pupil book pages 16–17.)
Skill: Students will identify and punctuate the four kinds of sentences.

T2

LANGUAGE AND USAGE

3 | Complete Subjects and Complete Predicates *(continued from page 5)*

B. Writing Application: A Ship's Report

Imagine that you are a navigator on a ship. Write five sentences to the captain, telling about the speed and direction of the ship. Draw a line between the complete subject and the complete predicate of each sentence. **Students to respond on separate paper. Answers will vary.**

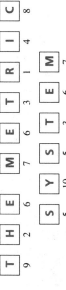

Enrichment

Draw a line between the complete subject and the complete predicate of each sentence.

1. The metric system | is a group of units.
   1   1
2. These units | measure length, temperature, or weight.
   2   2
3. Scientists | created the metric system.
   3   3
4. They | made the system logical and exact.
   4   4
5. Nonscientists | can learn the system easily.
   5   5
6. No other system of measurement | is as simple as the metric system.
   6   6
7. People | use the metric system in many countries.
   7   7
8. The term metric | comes from the system's basic unit of length.
   8   8
9. This basic unit of length | is the meter.
   9   9
10. A meter | is slightly longer than a yard.
    10   10

Now look at the complete predicates. Write the numbered letters from the complete predicates in the boxes below.

T	H	E		M	E	T	R	I	C
9	6	7		7	3	6	1	4	8

S	Y	S	T	E	M
5	10	5	3	6	7

Level 5 Unit 1 The Sentence *(Use with pupil book pages 18–19.)*
Skill: Students will identify complete subjects and complete predicates.

LANGUAGE AND USAGE

3 | Complete Subjects and Complete Predicates

Complete Subjects	Complete Predicates
A group of students	learned many new facts.
Weights and measures	fascinated them.

A. Underline each complete subject once. Underline each complete predicate twice.

1. The boys and girls studied different kinds of measures.
2. Some people of ancient times used cubits.
3. A cubit measured about twenty inches.
4. It was the distance from the elbow to the tip of the middle finger.
5. Ancient people based other units on body measurements.
6. Romans used the uncia as a unit of measurement.
7. The uncia was equivalent to the width of a person's thumb.
8. Twelve uncia equaled the length of a person's foot.
9. The differences in people's sizes made this system inaccurate.
10. The system failed because of this.
11. Modern systems of measurement are more exact.
12. The students wrote reports on modern measurement.
13. Mark and Nadia read about furlongs.
14. A furlong equals one-eighth of a mile.
15. Many of the students learned about nautical miles.
16. Nautical miles are longer than land miles.
17. A nautical mile equals about 6076 feet.
18. We call the speed of one nautical mile per hour a knot.
19. Modern ships and some planes report their speed in knots.
20. The sailors and pilots use knots in navigation as well.

(continued)

Level 5 Unit 1 The Sentence *(Use with pupil book pages 18–19.)*
Skill: Students will identify complete subjects and complete predicates.

Name _____

LANGUAGE AND USAGE

4 | **Simple Subjects** *(continued from page 7)*

WORKBOOK PLUS **8**

★ Enrichment ★

Underline the simple subject of each sentence.

1. Beautiful plants grow in the Everglades.
2. The sun often shines brightly.
3. Fish swim in the water.
4. Some plants provide shelter for the fish.
5. The fish in the Everglades are interesting.
6. Some fish are found only in warm waters.
7. Birds in the Everglades include wild turkeys and wading birds.
8. Most fish try to hide from the birds.
9. The large, fierce alligators do not fear the birds.
10. The birds flee from alligators.

Now complete this Everglades food chain. Write the simple subjects in the numbered blanks below.

Plants make food from the **sun** .
1   2

Little **fish** eat **plants** .
      3   4

Big **fish** eat little **fish** .
     5   6

Some **birds** eat big **fish** .
       7   8

Alligators eat some **birds** .
9   10

Level 5   Unit 1   The Sentence   *(Use with pupil book pages 20–21.)*
Skill: Students will identify simple subjects.

Name _____

LANGUAGE AND USAGE

4 | **Simple Subjects**

WORKBOOK PLUS **7**

> My older **cousin** from Houston traveled to Florida.
> The **Florida Everglades** was her first stop.
> **She** loved seeing the wildlife.
> The park's **beauty** impressed her.

A. Write the simple subject of each sentence.

1. Maria is my cousin. — **Maria**
2. She went on a trip to Florida last summer. — **She**
3. Maria's trip was interesting. — **trip**
4. Her family visited Everglades National Park. — **family**
5. Everglades National Park is mostly swamps. — **Everglades National Park**
6. A large part of the park is under water. — **part**
7. It contains many types of plants. — **It**
8. Some plants grow as high as seventy feet. — **plants**
9. Many animals live there. — **animals**
10. The park is known for its amphibian population. — **park**
11. Some birds stay there for the winter. — **birds**
12. They fly north for the summer. — **They**
13. The birds' routes have been traced. — **routes**
14. Visitors to the Everglades can see the routes. — **Visitors**

B. **Writing Application: Creative Writing**
You are spending five days in the land of Zog. There are beautiful plants and strange animals. Each day you see something new and different. Write a sentence for each day, describing a sight you have seen. Underline the simple subject of each sentence.
Students to respond on separate paper. Answers will vary.

(continued)

Level 5   Unit 1   The Sentence   *(Use with pupil book pages 20–21.)*
Skill: Students will identify simple subjects.

Left page (9)

Name _____

LANGUAGE AND USAGE WORKBOOK PLUS 9

5 | Simple Predicates

> Felicia **learned** about insects.
> She **has discovered** many interesting facts.

A. Write the simple predicate of each sentence.

1. Most people find cockroaches troublesome. — find
2. These household pests get into everything. — get
3. The history of these pests may surprise you. — may surprise
4. These insects are strange and amazing creatures. — are
5. The cockroach family might be 300 million years old! — might be
6. A roach's antennae discover tiny amounts of water. — discover
7. Four mouth feelers search for food. — search
8. Bristles cover its strong legs. — cover
9. Its legs make it one of the world's fastest insects. — make
10. A baby roach grows into an adult in ten weeks. — grows
11. Over 3500 kinds of roaches exist all over the world. — exist
12. Some scientists study cockroaches and other insects. — study
13. Such scientists are called entomologists. — are called
14. The scientists have learned respect for the insects. — have learned
15. The cockroach is a genius at survival. — is
16. It adapts easily to any environment. — adapts
17. Many other tiny creatures interest humans. — interest
18. You will read about one of them on the next page. — will read

B. Writing Application: A Description

Imagine that you are an insect. Write five sentences about your life. Underline each simple predicate. **Students to respond on separate paper. Answers will vary.**

(continued)

Level 5 Unit 1 The Sentence   (Use with pupil book pages 22–23.)
Skill: Students will identify and will write simple predicates.

Right page (10)

Name _____

LANGUAGE AND USAGE   WORKBOOK PLUS 10

5 | Simple Predicates   *(continued from page 9)*

Enrichment

Underline the simple predicate of each sentence below.

1. Hundreds or even thousands of these insects live together in colonies.
2. Some colonies have made mounds up to forty feet high!
3. The mounds contain homes for the insects.
4. Most of the insects are workers or soldiers.
5. These insects eat wood.
6. The insects damage property.
7. The insects' bodies can turn wood into food.
8. They have destroyed some buildings.

Now write the simple predicates in order on the lines below. Then follow the directions next to each line.

1. live — Circle the second letter.
2. have made — Circle the fourth letter.
3. contain — Circle the fourth letter.
4. are — Circle the second letter.
5. eat — Circle the first letter.
6. damage — Circle the third letter.
7. can turn — Circle the fourth letter.
8. have destroyed — Circle the seventh letter.

Unscramble the circled letters to spell the name of the insect discussed in the sentences above.

These insects are _____ termites _____.

Level 5 Unit 1 The Sentence   (Use with pupil book pages 22–23.)
Skill: Students will identify simple predicates.

T5

Name _____

LANGUAGE AND USAGE

6 | Subjects in Imperative Sentences (continued from page 11)

★ Enrichment ★

Complete this television advertisement for Tater potatoes. Write an imperative sentence under each television screen to show what each announcer is saying.
Sample answers:

1.

2. See what Tater potatoes can do for you.

3. Rush to your favorite supermarket.

4. Discover many delicious recipes.

Enjoy Tater potatoes for breakfast, lunch, or dinner.

Now make up your own advertisement for a new kind of food. Draw your advertisement on another piece of paper.

Level 5 Unit 1 The Sentence (Use with pupil book pages 24–25.)
Skill: Students will write imperative sentences.

Name _____

LANGUAGE AND USAGE

6 | Subjects in Imperative Sentences

> Declarative Sentence: **Joshua** mashed the potatoes.
> Imperative Sentence: **(You)** Mash the potatoes, please.

A. For each sentence, write *D* for declarative or *I* for imperative. Then write the simple subject of the sentence.

1. Potatoes are an ancient crop. D Potatoes
2. Tell me more about potatoes. I (You)
3. We eat the underground stem. D We
4. Please give me some more facts. I (You)
5. The vegetables first grew in South America. D vegetables
6. Spanish explorers took them to Europe. D explorers
7. Please explain how they were grown. I (You)
8. Inca Indians grew them in the mountains. D Inca Indians
9. They used potatoes to make a special flour. D They
10. Guess how the flour was made. I (You)
11. Let me think, please. I (You)
12. Show me how it was done. I (You)
13. The Incas mashed the potatoes with their feet. D Incas
14. Imagine walking on all those potatoes. I (You)
15. People still make potato flour today. D People
16. Please don't ask me to do the mashing. I (You)

B. Writing Application: Directions

Imagine that you have invented a new way of cooking potatoes. Write five or more sentences explaining your method. Include three imperative sentences. List the simple subject for each sentence you write. **Answers will vary. Students to respond on separate paper.**

(continued)

Level 5 Unit 1 The Sentence (Use with pupil book pages 24–25.)
Skill: Students will identify declarative and imperative sentences and their simple subjects.

LANGUAGE AND USAGE WORKBOOK PLUS ▲ 13

7 ‖ Conjunctions

> Scientists **and** other people use thermometers.
> Thermometers can indicate a fever, **but** they cannot cure it.
> They can measure warm weather **or** indicate cold weather.

A. Complete each sentence. Write the conjunction that has the meaning given in parentheses.

1. The Fahrenheit __and__ the Celsius are scales. (**joins together**)

2. Many people in the United States use Fahrenheit thermometers, __but__ in Canada the Celsius scale is used. (**shows contrast**)

3. Do you use a Fahrenheit thermometer, __or__ do you prefer a Celsius thermometer? (**shows choice**)

4. The two thermometers measure the same things __but__ do this in different ways. (**shows contrast**)

5. On the Fahrenheit scale, water freezes at 32 degrees, __but__ on the Celsius scale, it freezes at 0 degrees. (**shows contrast**)

6. The temperature of boiling water is 212 degrees Fahrenheit, __but__ it is 100 degrees Celsius. (**shows contrast**)

7. Announcers __and__ forecasters use either scale. (**joins together**)

8. They say "Fahrenheit," __or__ they say "Celsius" to let you know which one they are using. (**shows choice**)

9. Some announcers use __and__ report both scales. (**joins together**)

10. Listen to the weather report tomorrow morning __and__ find out which thermometer the announcer is using. (**joins together**)

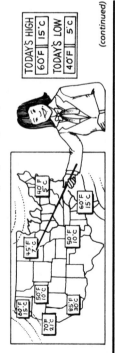

TODAY'S HIGH 60°F 15°C
TODAY'S LOW 40°F 5°C

(continued)

Level 5 Unit 1 The Sentence   *(Use with pupil book pages 26—27.)*
Skill: Students will use conjunctions in sentences.

T7

LANGUAGE AND USAGE WORKBOOK PLUS ▲ 14

7 ‖ Conjunctions *(continued from page 13)*

B. Writing Application: Sentences

Congratulations! You are going to be on television tonight. You will give the weather report. Write five sentences, telling what the weather will be like tomorrow. Use a conjunction in each sentence.
Students to respond on separate paper. Answers will vary.

Enrichment

The students in Mrs. Pizarro's class made up a game for conjunctions. In their game, *or* is worth 3 points, *but* is worth 2 points, and *and* is worth 1 point. Play the game by completing the following sentences with conjunctions. Write your points on the lines. WARNING: The conjunction must make sense in the sentence!
Sample answers:

1. Galileo made a thermometer, **but** _____ it was not accurate.   2

2. The device had a scale **and** _____ was called a thermoscope.   1

3. The thermometer used water **or** _____ other liquids.   3

4. The device didn't use alcohol, **but** _____ others did.   2

5. Did Fahrenheit **or** _____ Celsius first use mercury?   3

6. The first scales used boiling water, **or** _____ they used melting ice as a fixed temperature.   3

7. New thermometers use air **or** _____ work by electricity.   3

17

Add up your score. How many points did you get?

Stump a friend! On a separate sheet of paper, write five sentences in which more than one conjunction can make sense. Leave a blank line for each conjunction. See how many points your friend can get.

Page 16

Name _____

8 Combining Sentences: Compound Subjects (continued from page 15)

C. Writing Application: A Newspaper Article

You are a reporter in the mighty kingdom of Mook. You have just been to a ball at the royal palace. Now you must write an article for the *Mook Daily Journal*. Write at least five sentences, describing the king's and queen's clothes. Be sure to mention the colors. Include three or more sentences with compound subjects. **Students to respond on separate paper. Answers will vary.**

⭐ Enrichment ⭐

Tell about your dream house by completing the compound subjects below. **Answers will vary.**

1. _____ , _____ , and _____ live in my dream house.
2. _____ or _____ is the building material.
3. _____ , _____ , and _____ are the outside colors.
4. _____ or _____ is the color of the inside.
5. _____ or _____ is the color of my bedroom.
6. _____ , _____ , and _____ are in the yard.
7. _____ and _____ are secret places.
8. _____ or _____ is the location of the house.
9. _____ and _____ are in my room.
10. _____ and _____ are my favorite rooms.

Now draw the plan for your dream house on a separate piece of paper.

Page 15

Name _____

8 Combining Sentences: Compound Subjects

> **Simple Subjects:** **Elsa** will mix colors.
> **Eddie** will mix colors.
> **Compound Subject:** **Elsa** and **Eddie** will mix colors.

A. Underline each conjunction. Write the simple subjects in each compound subject.

1. Elsa and Luis were learning about colors. **Elsa, Luis**
2. A rainbow or a prism can show you many colors. **rainbow, prism**
3. Red, blue, and other colors make up a rainbow. **Red, blue, colors**
4. Red and yellow are primary colors. **Red, yellow**
5. Blue, yellow, and red can be combined to make other colors. **Blue, yellow, red**

B. Combine each group of sentences into one sentence with a compound subject. Use the conjunction shown in parentheses.

6. Elsa read about color vision. **(and)**
   Another student read about color vision.
   Elsa and another student read about color vision.
7. Heredity can be the cause of color blindness. **(or)**
   Disease can be the cause of color blindness.
   Heredity or disease can be the cause of color blindness.
8. Researchers have observed color vision in animals. **(and)**
   Pet owners have observed color vision in animals.
   Researchers and pet owners have observed color vision in animals.
9. Monkeys have color vision like humans. **(and)**
   Many birds have color vision like humans.
   Some fish have color vision like humans.
   Monkeys, many birds, and some fish have color vision like humans.

(continued)

T9

Page 17

9 ‖ Combining Sentences: Compound Predicates

Simple Predicates:	Phil **reads** many kinds of books.
	Phil **enjoys** many kinds of books.
Compound Predicate:	Phil **reads** and **enjoys** many kinds of books.

A. Underline each conjunction. Write the simple predicates in each compound predicate.

1. L. M. Montgomery's stories interest and amuse many readers. **interest, amuse**

2. She started as a teacher, married, and then became a writer. **started, married, became**

3. An editor saw Montgomery's work or knew her reputation. **saw, knew**

4. The editor met Montgomery, spoke to her, and asked her for a story. **met, spoke, asked**

5. She remembered and wrote about her days on Prince Edward Island. **remembered, wrote**

6. She added more adventures and created *Anne of Green Gables*. **added, created**

B. Combine each group of sentences into one sentence with a compound predicate. Use the conjunction in parentheses.

7. L. M. Montgomery wrote many other books. (and)
   L. M. Montgomery published many other books.
   L. M. Montgomery wrote and published many other books.

8. Many people buy Montgomery's books. (or)
   Many people borrow them from their friends.
   Many people take them out of the library.
   Many people buy Montgomery's books, borrow them from their friends, or take them out of the library.

(continued)

Page 18

9 ‖ Combining Sentences: Compound Predicates *(continued from page 17)*

C. Writing Application: A Book Review

Write five sentences about a book you have read. Tell something about the story and where it takes place. Explain why you did or did not like the book. Include three or more sentences with compound predicates in your review. *Students to respond on separate paper. Answers will vary.*

★ Enrichment ★

The travel guide below is all mixed-up. One simple predicate in each sentence is correct, but the other should be in a different sentence. Each incorrect predicate is underlined. Find the correct predicate in another sentence. Write the sentence correctly.

1. Prince Edward Island flies off Canada's coast and is its smallest province.
   Prince Edward Island lies off Canada's coast and is its smallest province.

2. Many people swim or live on Prince Edward Island.
   Many people visit or live on Prince Edward Island.

3. Some people sightsee or farm for a living.
   Some people fish or farm for a living.

4. Some farmers attract and sell potatoes.
   Some farmers grow and sell potatoes.

5. Sandy white beaches line the shore and grow tourists.
   Sandy white beaches line the shore and attract tourists.

6. Some tourists visit, ski, or sail in the water.
   Some tourists swim, ski, or sail in the water.

7. Other tourists fish and shop in the towns.
   Other tourists sightsee and shop in the towns.

8. A tourist takes a boat or lies to Prince Edward Island.
   A tourist takes a boat or flies to Prince Edward Island.

Name _____

LANGUAGE AND USAGE

10 | Combining Sentences: Compound Sentences *(continued from page 19)*

B. Writing Application: A Description

You have two fish named Floppy and Flippy. Although their names are alike, the fish are very different. Write five sentences, describing the fish and telling what they do. At least three of the sentences should be compound sentences.
Students to respond on separate paper. Answers will vary.

★ Enrichment ★

The poem below is about a very strange island. Complete the compound sentences to tell just how odd the island is. Make the last word of each sentence you write rhyme with the last word in the line above it.

The Island of Why

Sample answers:

Curtis lives on the island of Why.
There all birds can swim, **and all fish can fly.**

On the island of Why is a very strange town.
The ground is up, **and the sky is down.**

Why is odd, or so I've been told.
Grandparents are young, **but children are old.**

The island of Why must be quite a sight.
It's dark in the daytime, **and it's light at night.**

Level 5 Unit 1 The Sentence   *(Use with pupil book pages 32–33.)*
Skill: Students will write compound sentences.

Name _____

LANGUAGE AND USAGE

10 | Combining Sentences: Compound Sentences

Simple Sentences: Fish can live in an aquarium.
Water plants can live there too.
Compound Sentence: Fish can live in an aquarium, and water plants can live there too.

A. Combine each pair of sentences into a compound sentence. Use the conjunction that has the meaning given in parentheses. Use commas correctly.

1. Chen loves aquariums. He has never been to one. (shows contrast)
Chen loves aquariums, but he has never been to one.

2. The town has no aquarium. Chen has read about one. (shows contrast)
The town has no aquarium, but Chen has read about one.

3. He reads about the history. He discovers new facts. (joins together)
He reads about the history, and he discovers new facts.

4. Ancient Egyptians had aquariums. The Romans did too. (joins together)
Ancient Egyptians had aquariums, and the Romans did too.

5. They were popular in China. Japan also had them. (shows contrast)
They were popular in China, but Japan also had them.

6. Chen may visit an aquarium. He may make his own. (shows choice)
Chen may visit an aquarium, or he may make his own.

7. He could make an aquarium. He could buy one. (shows choice)
He could make an aquarium, or he could buy one.

8. Chen plans his aquarium. He chooses his fish. (joins together)
Chen plans his aquarium, and he chooses his fish.

(continued)

Level 5 Unit 1 The Sentence   *(Use with pupil book pages 32–33.)*
Skill: Students will combine simple sentences into compound sentences.

LANGUAGE AND USAGE

11 | Run-on Sentences

> **Run-on Sentence:** Helen lives in Arizona Tanya lives in Alaska.
> **Correct:** Helen lives in Arizona. Tanya lives in Alaska.
> **Also Correct:** Helen lives in Arizona, but Tanya lives in Alaska.

A. Correct these run-on sentences. First, separate each one into two sentences. Then write each one as a compound sentence.
Sample answers:

1. People dress one way for the cold they dress another way for the heat.

   Separate: **People dress one way for the cold. They dress another way for the heat.**

   Compound: **People dress one way for the cold, and they dress another way for the heat.**

2. Some clothes keep you warm some keep you cool.

   Separate: **Some clothes keep you warm. Some keep you cool.**

   Compound: **Some clothes keep you warm, and some keep you cool.**

3. Wool is warm cotton is cool.

   Separate: **Wool is warm. Cotton is cool.**

   Compound: **Wool is warm, but cotton is cool.**

4. Heat escapes from your head a hat can keep you warm.

   Separate: **Heat escapes from your head. A hat can keep you warm.**

   Compound: **Heat escapes from your head, but a hat can keep you warm.**

5. White clothes reflect the sun they keep you cool.

   Separate: **White clothes reflect the sun. They keep you cool.**

   Compound: **White clothes reflect the sun, and they keep you cool.**

(continued)

LANGUAGE AND USAGE

11 | Run-on Sentences *(continued from page 21)*

B. Writing Application: A Letter

You have just moved to the North Pole. Write a letter to your friend in Florida. Tell your friend about your life. Be sure you do not write any run-on sentences. Students to respond on separate paper. Answers will vary.

★ Enrichment ★

This radio announcer was so excited about a new product that she ran all of her sentences together! Help her by rewriting the advertisement. Correct each run-on sentence.

> Thermesh is a new space-age material it is made of special metallic fibers no other fiber is like thermesh it will keep you warm in the winter it will keep you cool in the summer it never needs ironing it won't crush, tear, or rust thermesh is water-proof use it as a tent it is soft enough for a baby's blanket you will never find another fabric like thermesh why should you settle for less this miracle material is not sold in stores supplies are limited don't miss your chance order thermesh today!

Sample answer:

Thermesh is a new space-age material. It is made of special metallic fibers. No other fiber is like thermesh. It will keep you warm in the winter. It will keep you cool in the summer. It never needs ironing. It won't crush, tear, or rust. Thermesh is waterproof. Use it as a tent! It is soft enough for a baby's blanket. You will never find another fabric like thermesh. Why should you settle for less? This miracle material is not sold in stores. Supplies are limited. Don't miss your chance. Order thermesh today!

UNIT 2 TEACHER'S ANNOTATED PAGES

Name _____

COMPOSITION SKILL: PERSONAL NARRATIVE

WORKBOOK PLUS 24

Supplying Details

Poor Detail: I was nervous.
Interesting Detail: My palms were sweating and my knees were shaking as I walked to the front of the room.

Read the following paragraphs. Then rewrite each paragraph, adding details to make each one more interesting.

A. The wind was howling. I looked out the window at the street. It was empty. I saw a trash can blow over and roll down the street. A branch of a tree broke. It fell onto the roof next door.

Answers will vary.

_____

_____

_____

B. It was my first day at a new school. I was so scared that I walked into the wrong classroom at first. Finally I found my room. Everyone looked at me. The teacher moved toward me and said hello. Then I tripped.

Answers will vary.

_____

_____

_____

Level 5 Unit 2 Personal Narrative (Use with pupil book page 65.)
Skill: Students will rewrite paragraphs, adding details for interest.

Name _____

COMPOSITION SKILL: PERSONAL NARRATIVE

WORKBOOK PLUS 23

Writing a Good Beginning

Poor Beginning: Last week was my grandmother's birthday. We had a party.
Better Beginning: Have you ever tried to blow out sixty candles at once?

A. Write two good beginnings for each of the stories below. Put a check next to the one you like better.
Sample answers:
1. . . . The lights had never before gone out when I was home alone. I felt my way along the walls, found the light switch, and flicked it up and down. Nothing happened. "Now what?" I asked myself.

Beginning: ✓ **One minute I was watching television, and the next minute I was in total darkness.**

Beginning: **"Don't worry, Mom, I'll be fine," I'd said to my mother before she left.**

2. . . . The line for the roller coaster was getting shorter. My turn would be coming any minute. I was nervous about my first ride. Would I be scared? Excited? Sick? I swallowed hard.

Beginning: **How does it feel to ride on a roller coaster for the first time? I was about to find out.**

Beginning: ✓ **It was too late to back out.**

B. Think of a funny, sad, or frightening experience that you have had or have observed. Write two good beginnings for a story about what happened. Put a check next to the better beginning.

Beginning: **Answers will vary.**

Beginning:

Level 5 Unit 2 Personal Narrative (Use with pupil book page 64.)
Skill: Students will write two good beginnings for stories and will choose the better one.

T12

T13

Writing Dialogue

> "Use quotation marks whenever you write dialogue," said Mrs. Garcia. Chris added, "Begin a new paragraph for each change of speaker too."

A. Rewrite the sentences below as a dialogue. Put quotation marks around the exact words that each person might say. Try to make the dialogue sound the way people really talk.

Ari said that he had an idea. I asked him what it was. He said that we should go swimming. I agreed.   Sample answers:

"Hey, I have an idea," Ari said.

"What?" I asked him.

"Let's go swimming," he suggested.

"Okay," I answered.

B. Look at the illustration below. Write a dialogue between the two characters. Write at least two sentences for each character.   Sample answers:

Grandma said, "When I was a girl, I walked five miles to

school every day."

"Why didn't you take the school bus?" asked Sunny.

"There were no buses," answered Grandma.

Sunny asked, "Couldn't anyone drive you?"

"There were very few cars back then," Grandma replied.

Writing a Good Title

> **Poor Title:** My Sister's Pet Hamster Sleepy
> **Good Title:** Why I Hate Hamsters

Read each story below. Write two good titles for each one. Underline the title that you like better in each pair.   Sample answers:

A.   The Bus Station

The Long Wait

I felt as if I had been waiting for hours. I began to worry. Maybe no one would come to meet me after all. At least I wasn't alone. The bus station was crowded with travelers. As I waited, I tried to imagine where they had come from or where they were going. I was daydreaming so much that I hardly noticed the familiar face in the crowd.

B.   A Visit to Carlsbad Caverns

Living in New Mexico

One of my favorite things about living in New Mexico is visiting Carlsbad Caverns. A guide shows visitors huge underground rocks that look like giant icicles. They are called stalactites and stalagmites. There are very few living things in the caves. However, there is one cave called the Bat Cave. It is my favorite.

C.   Snorkeling with My Sister

Underwater Adventure

I went snorkeling with my sister. The instructor gave us each a mask with a breathing tube. We saw crabs, clam shells, and beautifully colored fish. Being underwater felt mysterious. I can't wait to go again!

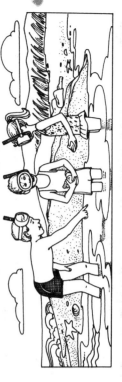

Name _____

THE WRITING PROCESS: PERSONAL NARRATIVE

Step 3: Revise

Have I

changed the beginning so that it will catch a reader's attention?

added details that give a clear picture?

added dialogue that brings the characters to life?

written an interesting title that does not tell too much?

yes

☐ ☐ ☐ ☐

Revise the following story. Use the check list above to help you. Check off each box when you have finished your revision.
• Use the space above each line, on the sides, and below the paragraph for your changes.
Sample answers:

                          An Exciting Sail
                  ~~Going Sailing for the First Time~~

    "Alicia," called Dad. "Would you like to go sailing with me? It's a
                            ⌃ I'd love
perfect day for sailing. ~~My dad asked me if I wanted to go sailing. He said it was a~~
~~perfect day. The wind was just right for sailing. I told Dad I~~
~~would like to go.~~ The wind is strong and steady!"⌃ I told Dad
to go!" I yelled back.   It is sparkling white with two large, red
sails. ~~If you saw it, you~~ Dad's boat is really pretty.⌃ It has a long, sleek body, called a hull. It's designed to go fast. ~~would know that it was designed to go fast.~~ Dad pushed us away

from the dock. I hoisted the mainsail, and it filled with wind.
           slowly   ⌃ Dad said, "Pull
The boat sailed⌃ across the water, making little waves. ~~Dad said~~
a little tighter on the sail. That's the rope attached to the sail."
~~to pull a little tighter on the sheet. That's the rope attached to~~
         sharply   ⌃ "I'm scared, Dad!"
~~the sail.~~ I did, and the boat leaned⌃to one side. ~~I told Dad that I~~
I shouted. ⌃ "Don't worry," he said. "We're just heeling." ~~was scared, but he explained that we were just heeling.~~ The boat
       like lightning! We zoomed through the water.
moved ~~very fast.~~ It was very exciting!

Level 5 Unit 2 Personal Narrative   (Use with pupil book pages 71–72.)
Skill: Students will revise a story, changing the title and the beginning, and adding details and dialogue.

Name _____

THE WRITING PROCESS: PERSONAL NARRATIVE

Step 4: Proofread

                       deep   diggers
      the hole was ~~dep~~ and the ~~diggers~~ were tired.
                 ≡

Proofreading Marks

¶ Indent.
⌃ Add something.
𝓎 Take out something.
≡ Capitalize.
/ Make a small letter.

A. Proofread the following story. Find three mistakes in spelling, one mistake in capitalization, one missing end mark, one run-on sentence, and one mistake in a compound sentence. Use proofreading marks to correct the mistakes. Use a dictionary to check your spelling.

"How many pennies are in the jar?" Mr. Phipp asked when we came into his
                              careful 𝓎
store. I took a ~~carefull~~ look at the jar. It was big and the pennies were piled to the
                                                          letters 𝓎   number
top. I took a wild guess, there are six ~~letters~~ in my name. Mr. Phipp's store is at
                                         ≡   ≡   ~~nuber~~ of
102 Main Street. I multiplied 102 by 6. that came to 612, the exact ~~nuber~~ of
                                          ≡

pennies in the jar!

B. Proofread this story. There are four mistakes in spelling, one mistake in end punctuation, and one mistake in a compound sentence. Correct the mistakes.

                                                            lose 𝓎
    In the night I had an idea for a story. I didn't want to ~~loose~~ it. I grabbed
     paper
some ~~papr~~ It was on my desk. I wrote some notes and got back into bed. The
                                                    excited
                                         ⌃ dream
story idea was great and I was ~~exited~~ about it! The next morning I couldn't find
                                              dream
my notes 𝓎. The story idea and my notes had all been a ~~drem~~!

Level 5 Unit 2 Personal Narrative   (Use with pupil book pages 73–74.)
Skill: Students will proofread a story, correcting mistakes in spelling, punctuation, and capitalization.

Page 29

Name _____

1 | What Is a Noun?

Persons:	relative	Sara	Uncle Ed
Places:	bay	Hudson Bay	Bay of Fundy
Things:	games	Olympics	baseball
Ideas:	safety	problem	agreement

A. Write the nouns in each sentence.

1. My aunt works at Woods Hole as a scientist.
   aunt, Woods Hole, scientist

2. Aunt Jane has an understanding of the habits of whales.
   Aunt Jane, understanding, habits, whales

3. These mammals spend their entire life in the sea.
   mammals, life, sea

4. These animals are the largest creatures on earth.
   animals, creatures, earth

5. Their brains may be as big as watermelons.
   brains, watermelons

6. Biologists are studying ways to measure their intelligence.
   Biologists, ways, intelligence

7. Some species that have neared extinction are now protected.
   species, extinction

8. New laws in the United States call for their protection.
   laws, United States, protection

B. Writing Application: A Paragraph

Imagine that you have suddenly become as big as a whale! Write a paragraph, telling about things you can and cannot do because of your size. Circle each noun in your paragraph.
Students to respond on separate paper. Answers will vary.   *(continued)*

Level 5   Unit 3 Nouns   *(Use with pupil book pages 82–83.)*
Skill: Students will identify and will use nouns.

Page 30

Name _____

1 | What Is a Noun?   *(continued from page 29)*

Enrichment

Below is a map of Blue Bay. Here are some symbols used on the map:

lighthouse   dock   whale

lifeguard   water   ship

Use the map to find the answers to the questions. Write a complete sentence for each answer. Underline the nouns in your sentences.

Sample answers:

1. Where are the two lighthouses?
   The lighthouses are at Finleytown and at Gresham.

2. Which town is closest to the large ship?
   Finleytown is closest to the large ship.

3. On which beach is there a lifeguard?
   There is a lifeguard on Ames Beach.

4. Where can people keep their boats?
   People can keep their boats at the dock at Old Port.

5. Where is the largest school of whales?
   The largest school of whales is near Sunlight Beach.

Level 5   Unit 3 Nouns   *(Use with pupil book pages 82–83.)*
Skill: Students will use nouns in sentences.

Name _____ WORKBOOK PLUS **32**

LANGUAGE AND USAGE

2 | Singular and Plural Nouns (continued from page 31)

B. Writing Application: Sentences

You are a zoo keeper. Choose five kinds of animals in your zoo and write a sentence, telling what you will feed each of them tomorrow. Use the plural forms of five nouns from the box below.

fox	nuthatch	puppy	skunk
monkey	octopus	rhinoceros	snake

Students to respond on separate paper. Answers will vary.

★ Enrichment ★

Write a table of contents for a book about animals. The title for each chapter should include the plural form of a noun from the box below. Be sure that each chapter has an interesting title!

jay	walrus	turkey	ostrich	fly
donkey	puppy	guppy	fox	thrush
monkey	bunny	pony	moth	panda

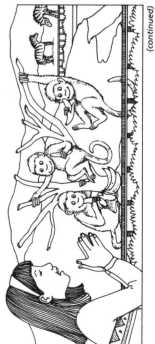

Table of Contents

	page
_____	5
_____	10
_____	17
_____	21
_____	25
_____	32
_____	36
_____	40

Answers will vary.

Level 5 Unit 3 Nouns *(Use with pupil book pages 84–85.)*
Skill: Students will write the plural forms of regular nouns.

Name _____ WORKBOOK PLUS **31**

LANGUAGE AND USAGE

2 | Singular and Plural Nouns

Singular Nouns	Plural Nouns	Singular Nouns	Plural Nouns
cat	cats	finch	finches
dove	doves	thrush	thrushes
walrus	walruses	donkey	donkeys
fox	foxes	pony	ponies

A. If the underlined noun is singular, write the plural form. If it is plural, write the singular form.

1. Aki visited the animals in the zoos. — **animal, zoo**
2. She watched the zebras gallop through the pass. — **zebra, passes**
3. The lynx cared for the baby. — **lynxes, babies**
4. The monkey ate the bunch of bananas. — **monkeys, bunches**
5. Aki heard the crash when the chimp threw a pan. — **crashes, chimps**
6. Aki watched the lizards play around the cactus. — **lizard, cactuses**
7. The parrot was picking the berry from the bush. — **berries, bushes**
8. The jay sat on the perch. — **jays, perches**
9. The fox slept in the small hutch. — **foxes, hutches**
10. Aki told the class about her adventures. — **classes, adventure**

(continued)

Level 5 Unit 3 Nouns *(Use with pupil book pages 84–85.)*
Skill: Students will write the singular and plural forms of regular nouns.

LANGUAGE AND USAGE

3 | **More Plural Nouns**   *(continued from page 33)*

B. Writing Application: A Paragraph

Write a paragraph about something you do or would like to do in your spare time. Use the plural forms of at least four nouns from the box below.

| radio | shelf | banjo | hero | tooth |
| piano | life | studio | foot | stereo |

Students to respond on separate paper. Answers will vary.

★ Enrichment ★

Fabia Howl is writing rhyming word pairs for her new operetta. You can help her by combining the syllables in the notes to form nouns. Write the plural form of each noun next to its definition.

1.	vegetables	**potatoes**	, reddish fruits	**tomatoes**
2.	singers	**altos**	, singers	**sopranos**
3.	wireless sets	**radios**	, artists' workrooms	**studios**
4.	brave persons	**heroes**	, numbers	**zeroes**
5.	musical instruments	**banjos**	, musical instruments	**pianos**

LANGUAGE AND USAGE

3 | **More Plural Nouns**

Singular Nouns	Plural Nouns	Singular Nouns	Plural Nouns
leaf	leaves	hero	heroes
giraffe	giraffes	foot	feet
banjo	banjos	deer	deer

A. Write the plural form of the noun in parentheses to complete each sentence. You may use your dictionary.

1. Opera lovers can listen to opera on their ___**radios**___ . (radio)

2. Yesterday Murray heard some ___**women**___ sing. (woman)

3. They were ___**sopranos**___ . (soprano)

4. Women with lower voices are called ___**altos**___ . (alto)

5. Some ___**men**___ are tenors, and others are baritones. (man)

6. ___**Children**___ sometimes sing in operas too. (child)

7. ___**Pianos**___ and other instruments accompany the singers. (piano)

8. Murray reads about the ___**lives**___ of opera stars. (life)

9. According to his ___**beliefs**___ , they are the best singers. (belief)

10. He says some popular singers sound like ___**moose**___ ! (moose)

11. He grits his ___**teeth**___ when he hears those singers. (tooth)

12. He likes opera singers to sing ___**solos**___ . (solo)

13. He likes the ___**echoes**___ their voices make. (echo)

14. Murray finds many ___**ways**___ to follow his interest. (way)

15. He hopes to visit some recording ___**studios**___ . (studio)

16. He thinks that ___**stereos**___ reproduce music very well. (stereo)

17. His ___**shelves**___ are filled with records. (shelf)

18. Murray hopes to attend two opera ___**series**___ next year. (series)

(continued)

Name _____

LANGUAGE AND USAGE

4 | Common and Proper Nouns

Common Nouns	Proper Nouns
ranger	Joe Garcia
place	Grand Canyon
month	June
holiday	Fourth of July

A. Underline the nouns in each group of sentences. Then write the proper nouns, using capital letters correctly. The numbers in parentheses tell how many common and proper nouns are in each group of sentences.

1. Last <u>july</u> my <u>family</u> visited <u>banff national park</u> in the <u>province</u> of <u>alberta</u>. <u>banff</u> is among the oldest <u>parks</u> in <u>canada</u> and covers more than 2500 square <u>miles</u>. (9)
   July, Banff National Park, Alberta, Banff, Canada

2. Our <u>group</u> camped near <u>lake louise</u> on the <u>fourth of july</u> and spent two after-<u>noons</u> at the <u>lake</u>. Many special <u>exhibits</u> and informative <u>lectures</u> were offered in the nearby <u>lodge</u>. (8)
   Lake Louise, Fourth of July

3. One <u>day</u> all of the <u>visitors</u> took a <u>tour</u> through <u>cascade rock gardens</u>. The <u>guide</u> was <u>hilda revels</u>. The <u>hikers</u> took a <u>trail</u> up <u>sulphur mountain</u>. The <u>view</u> from the <u>top</u> was spectacular. Later, <u>miss revels</u> pointed out the <u>mountaintops</u>. (13)
   Cascade Rock Gardens, Hilda Revels, Sulphur Mountain, Miss Revels

4. In <u>january</u> people skate and ski in the <u>mountains</u>. <u>Tourists</u> can ride through the <u>rocky mountains</u> in a <u>sleigh</u>. (6)
   January, Rocky Mountains

5. In <u>june</u> the <u>springs</u> and beautiful <u>scenery</u> attract <u>travelers</u> from the <u>united states</u>, <u>europe</u>, and even <u>japan</u>. (7)
   June, United States, Europe, Japan

(continued)

Level 5   Unit 3 Nouns   (Use with pupil book pages 88–89.)
Skill: Students will identify common and proper nouns.

Name _____

LANGUAGE AND USAGE

4 | Common and Proper Nouns   (continued from page 35)

B. Writing Application: A Travel Poster

Make a poster to encourage people to visit your town. Draw a picture of a sight that would interest tourists. Then write five sentences on your poster, explaining why your town is interesting. Underline the common nouns on your poster. Circle the proper nouns.

Students to respond on separate paper. Answers will vary.

Enrichment

Look at the meanings of the following symbols. Rewrite the paragraph below. Replace each symbol with the name of a person, a place, or a thing. Capitalize the proper nouns.

☆ a person   ☐ a place   ☆ a thing

So far the ☆ had gone well. I was proud to be testing my ☆. I got to the ☐ and saw the ☆. Now I was getting nervous. Still I wanted the ☆. There was no turning back. ☆ and ☺ had helped me before. Now it was my turn. I made it to the ☐, and there before me was the ☐. I heard a ☆ and then a ☆. What was happening? I turned in time to see the ☆ coming from the ☐. I tried to do something, but my ☆ seemed frozen in fright. Suddenly I heard the voices of the ☺ behind me. What a ☆ !

Answers will vary.

Level 5   Unit 3 Nouns   (Use with pupil book pages 88–89.)
Skill: Students will use common and proper nouns.

5 | Singular Possessive Nouns

Singular Nouns	Singular Possessive Nouns
friend	friend's team
student	student's bat
Amos	Amos's decision

A. Rewrite each sentence. Change the underlined group of words to include a singular possessive noun.

1. The book belonging to Amos is on the first black player in the major leagues.
   Amos's book is on the first black player in the major leagues.

2. The name of this baseball player is Jackie Robinson.
   This baseball player's name is Jackie Robinson.

3. The book is the autobiography of Robinson.
   The book is Robinson's autobiography.

4. The playing of this second baseman attracted attention.
   This second baseman's playing attracted attention.

5. The average that this batter had was the highest in the league.
   This batter's average was the highest in the league.

6. The skills that the athlete had earned him a place with the Dodgers.
   The athlete's skills earned him a place with the Dodgers.

7. The talents of the player won him the Spingarn Medal.
   The player's talents won him the Spingarn Medal.

8. The election of the sports star to the Hall of Fame was in 1962.
   The sports star's election to the Hall of Fame was in 1962.

(continued)

---

5 | Singular Possessive Nouns *(continued from page 37)*

B. Writing Application: A Paragraph

Write a paragraph about a real or an imaginary sports star. Explain why the star is famous. Include four or more singular possessive nouns in your paragraph. **Students to respond on separate paper. Answers will vary.**

Enrichment

Here is the equipment some students brought with them to play a new game called Jump Fast:

Explain how the students above will play Jump Fast, using the equipment they have with them. Write a possessive noun and another noun in each blank.
Sample answers:

Jenny will hit ___**Katie's ball**___ with ___**Ramon's racket**___ .

The ball will bounce over ___**Jenny's net**___ ...Amos must skip once

with ___**Lisa's rope**___ before Katie catches the ball

in ___**Amos's glove**___ .

Now invent another game that can be played with the same equipment. On a separate piece of paper, explain how to play the game. Use singular possessive nouns in your explanation.

T19

Page 39

LANGUAGE AND USAGE

6 | Plural Possessive Nouns

Plural Nouns	Plural Possessive Nouns
bats	**bats'** wings
ladies	**ladies'** shoes
geese	**geese's** feathers
elk	**elk's** teeth

A. Rewrite each sentence. Change the underlined group of words to include a plural possessive noun.

1. The names of the Marx brothers were Groucho, Harpo, and Chico.
   The Marx brothers' names were Groucho, Harpo, and Chico.

2. The acting of the Marxes was famous.
   The Marxes' acting was famous.

3. The first public appearance the actors had was on the stage.
   The actors' first public appearance was on the stage.

4. The jokes of the men were funny.
   The men's jokes were funny.

5. Later, movies by these heroes were popular.
   Later, these heroes' movies were popular.

6. Perhaps the favorite of the children was Harpo.
   Perhaps the children's favorite was Harpo.

7. Harpo and Chico played music in the films of these stars.
   Harpo and Chico played music in these stars' films.

8. The instruments these musicians owned were a harp and a piano.
   These musicians' instruments were a harp and a piano.

(continued)

Level 5 Unit 3 Nouns *(Use with pupil book pages 92–93.)*
Skill: Students will write the possessive forms of plural nouns.

Page 40

LANGUAGE AND USAGE

6 | Plural Possessive Nouns *(continued from page 39)*

B. Writing Application: A Movie Review

Write five sentences about a movie that you have seen. Tell what the stars did. Explain why you did or did not like the movie. Include at least three plural possessive nouns in your review.
Students to respond on separate paper. Answers will vary.

Enrichment ★

Hilda Highbrow is reviewing a new musical group. Help her write her review. Use the details in the picture to help you write the sentences. Use the word in parentheses and a plural possessive noun in each sentence.

Answers will vary.

1. (pianos) _____

2. (horns) _____

3. (harps) _____

4. (drums) _____

5. (violins) _____

Level 5 Unit 3 Nouns *(Use with pupil book pages 92–93.)*
Skill: Students will write the possessive forms of plural nouns.

Page 41

Main Idea of a Paragraph

> A paragraph is made up of sentences that tell about one topic.
> The sentences discuss one main idea about the topic.

Read the following paragraphs. Write the main idea of each paragraph in your own words. Draw a line through any sentence that does not tell about the main idea.

Sample answer:

A.   When you can no longer tell what color your leather shoes are, it may be time to clean them. ~~Most kids wear sneakers every day.~~ Besides your dirty shoes, you will need a shoe brush, a soft cloth, and shoe polish. First, use the brush to remove any loose dirt from the shoes. ~~Rain and snow are very bad for leather shoes.~~ Then put some polish on the cloth and spread it evenly over the shoes. Rub the polish lightly into the leather. Finally, rub the shoes briskly with a clean, soft cloth until they shine.

Main Idea: __Here is a way to clean dirty shoes.__

B.   What should you do if you are the only one to see a serious accident? If you think fast, you can help the injured person. The first thing to remember is to stay calm. If an adult is nearby, shout for help. If not, find a telephone and speak with the telephone operator. ~~An operator's job must be exciting.~~ Tell the operator your name, where you are, and what has happened. The operator will call the proper people for help. Go back to the person who is hurt and try to keep him or her calm until help arrives.

Main Idea: __If you are the only person to see a serious accident, keep calm and help.__

Page 42

Topic Sentences and Supporting Details

> The **topic sentence** of a paragraph clearly states the main idea.
> The other sentences give **supporting details** about the main idea.

A.   Each paragraph below needs a topic sentence. Read each paragraph and write two different topic sentences for it. Then put a check next to the topic sentence that you like better.

Sample answers:

   You can buy plant foods in liquid or in powder form. Carefully read the directions on the back of the container. Mix the food with water exactly as the directions tell you. You may harm your plants if you do not use the correct amount of plant food. Plants in clay pots usually need more plant food than those in plastic pots. Plants that sit or hang in a bright, sunny window need more food than those that are placed in a shadier spot. Feeding your plants once or twice a month is usually often enough. If the soil in a pot is white and crusty on top, you are feeding that plant too much.

Topic Sentence 1: __It is important to feed your houseplants correctly.__

Topic Sentence 2: __You can feed your houseplants with either liquid or powdered plant food.__

   Check all your plants often for insects. Even before buying a new plant, check for bugs. When you do bring a new plant home, set it apart from your other plants until you are sure it has no bugs. If you do find that some insects are living in your plants, separate affected plants from the others while you try to get rid of the bugs. You are less likely to have insects harm your plants if you keep the plants healthy and clean.

Topic Sentence 1: __You can protect your houseplants from insects.__

Topic Sentence 2: __Houseplants are often attacked by insects.__

(continued)

Name _____

Step-by-Step Order

When you write a paragraph of instructions, put the steps in an order that makes sense. Use order words such as *first, next, then,* and *finally* to help make the order clear.

A. The following paragraph gives instructions for making modeling dough. However, the instructions are all mixed up! Rewrite the paragraph, putting the instructions in order. Add order words to help make the order clear.
Sample answer:

Knead in food coloring. Put one cup of salt and one-half cup of cornstarch into a saucepan. Add two-thirds of a cup of water. Remove the pan from the heat. Cook over low heat, stirring constantly until the mixture becomes a thick mass. Cool the mixture until you can handle it easily. Use the dough immediately or put it into a covered jar and store it in the refrigerator.

First, put one cup of salt and one-half cup of cornstarch

into a saucepan. Next, add two-thirds of a cup of water. Cook

over low heat, stirring constantly until the mixture becomes a

thick mass. Then remove the pan from the heat. Cool the

mixture until you can handle it easily. Finally, knead in food

coloring. Use the dough immediately or put it into a covered

jar and store it in the refrigerator.

_____

_____

B. Now write a topic sentence for the paragraph of instructions you have just rewritten. Sample answer:

You can make modeling dough by following a few simple

steps.

_____

Level 5 Unit 4 Instructions *(Use with pupil book pages 125–126.)*
Skill: Students will rewrite a paragraph of instructions in order, using order words, and will write a topic
sentence for the paragraph.

Name _____

Topic Sentences and Supporting Details *(continued from page 42)*

B. Read each paragraph below. Think of supporting details you can add to each one. Then rewrite the paragraph, adding two or three more sentences with supporting details. Underline the topic sentence of each paragraph.

Fruit salad is delicious and easy to make. You can use almost any kind of fruit. Add some fruit-flavored yogurt and stir everything together. Then cover the bowl and chill it until you are ready to eat. Yum! Sample answer:

Fruit salad is delicious and easy to make. You can use

almost any kind of fruit. Berries, melon, and bananas are good

together. Chopped nuts are good in it too. First, wash the fruit

and cut the peel from the melon if you are using one. Cut up

the fruit and put it in a large bowl. Add some fruit-flavored

yogurt. Strawberry is a good choice. Stir everything together.

Then cover the bowl and chill it until you are ready to eat.

Yum!

You can make your own rubber stamp. You will need a small block of wood, some thick rubber bands, scissors, a pencil, rubber cement, a stamp pad, and paper. First, draw a simple design on the woodblock with the pencil. Then cut pieces of rubber band to fit the outline of your design. Glue the rubber-band pieces in place, using the rubber cement. Now ink your stamp and try it on the paper. Sample answer:

You can make your own rubber stamp. You will need a small

block of wood, some thick rubber bands, scissors, a pencil,

rubber cement, a stamp pad, and paper. First, draw a simple

design on the woodblock with the pencil. You could draw an

arrow or a star. Then cut pieces of rubber band to fit the

outline of your design. Try to make the outline sharp. Glue the

rubber-band pieces in place, using the rubber cement. Don't

use too much rubber cement. Now ink your stamp and try it

on the paper.

Step 3: Revise

Have I

added a topic sentence?

circled sentences that are out of order and drawn arrows to
show where they belong?

added order words to make the order clearer?

replaced unclear words with exact nouns?

yes
☐

☐
☐
☐

Revise the following instructions for making a terrarium. Use the check list
above to help you. Check off each box when you have finished your revision.

• Use a thesaurus to choose exact words.
• Use the space above each line, on the sides, and below the paragraph for
your changes.

Sample answers:

A terrarium is easy to make.   jar   a
You will need a large glass container with something tight to
               small   house
cover it, pebbles, potting soil, and green plants that aren't very
lid
                                     jar   Next,
First,   glass thing. Add
big. Put a layer of pebbles in the bottom of the
                            just damp
a thin layer of
the potting soil. Moisten the soil until it is wet but not muddy.
                                 Then   little house.
Finally,   the lid   jar
Put something tight over the container. Place the plants in
                         sunny
the soil
firmly. Put your terrarium in a bright place, but not in the direct
           enjoy your own miniature plant world
sun. Now feel good about this small plant world.

Level 5   Unit 4 Instructions   (Use with pupil book pages 131–132.)
Skill: Students will revise a paragraph of instructions, adding a topic sentence and order words, putting steps
in correct sequence, and replacing unclear words with exact nouns.

Purpose and Audience

Purpose and audience affect what you say and how you say it.
Some purposes for writing are to explain, to entertain, or to persuade.
Some audiences are classmates, friends, teachers, and relatives.

Write the purpose and the audience for each of the following writing
situations.

Sample answers:

1. Pam wrote a report about the American bald eagle for science class.

   Purpose: to explain

   Audience: Pam's science teacher and science class

2. Eric left a note on the refrigerator, asking his sister to please feed and walk the
dog for him that night.

   Purpose: to persuade

   Audience: Eric's sister

3. Becky's friend wanted to make balloon animals for some six-year-olds at a
birthday party. Becky wrote directions for her.

   Purpose: to explain

   Audience: Becky's friend

4. Your letter about why children should be given free admission to local museums
appeared in your local newspaper.

   Purpose: to persuade

   Audience: readers of your local newspaper

5. Matt wrote a story for his best friend about the funniest thing that ever happened to him.

   Purpose: to entertain

   Audience: Matt's best friend

Name _____

LANGUAGE AND USAGE

1 Action Verbs

Elizabeth **likes** art.
Yesterday she **painted** a beautiful picture.

A. Write the action verb in each sentence.

1. Elizabeth went to an artist's studio.   went

2. She watched the artist carefully.   watched

3. Elizabeth envied the potter's ability.   envied

4. Elizabeth started a pottery club at school.   started

5. A different potter comes each week.   comes

6. The potters instruct the students.   instruct

7. Elizabeth follows the instructions carefully.   follows

8. First, she kneads the clay.   kneads

9. Then she throws a lump of clay onto the potter's wheel.   throws

10. She slowly turns the heavy wheel with her foot.   turns

11. Elizabeth wets her hands in a bowl of water.   wets

12. Her fingers shape the clay.   shape

13. She forms the clay into a mug.   forms

14. Then she molds a piece of clay into a handle.   molds

15. The students place the mugs in a special oven. place

16. The clay bakes in the kiln for several hours.   bakes

17. Then the students put glaze on their mugs.   put

18. Some students paint designs on their work.   paint

19. They return their mugs to the kiln.   return

20. The students display their work at the art fair.   display

(continued)

Level 5   Unit 5 Verbs   *(Use with pupil book pages 142–143.)*
Skill: Students will identify action verbs.

Name _____

THE WRITING PROCESS: INSTRUCTIONS

Step 4: Proofread

whole
the hole Class discussed children's hobbies hobbys.

Proofreading Marks

¶ Indent.
∧ Add something.
𝒆 Take out something.
≡ Capitalize.
/ Make a small letter.

A. Proofread the following paragraph. There are two spelling mistakes, two mistakes in forming plurals, one punctuation error, one capitalization error, one run-on sentence, and one mistake in paragraph format. Use proofreading marks to correct the mistakes. Use a dictionary to check your spelling.

¶ You can make finger paint at home. Put one cup of laundry starch, one cup of
                                                                          cups
cool water, and two cupes of hot water into a large saucepan. Cook over low
                                                                          flakes
heat until the mixture is thick turn off the stove. Add one cup of soap flake to
                                                                                    you're
the saucepan. Stir well. The texture of the paint should be thick and smooth.
       four
Divide the paint into for jars. stir some food coloring into each jar. Now your
ready to paint!

B. Proofread the following paragraph. There are two spelling mistakes, two mistakes in forming plurals, one error in punctuation, one capitalization error, and one run-on sentence. Correct the mistakes.

                                                             prints
Use your paints to make vegetable printes. Line a plate with several paper towels.
                                                                          add a few drops of
Spread the paint evenly over the towels to make a stamp pad.
                                                                          potatoes
liquid detergent to the paint slice some vegetables. For example, use potatos,
mushrooms, or cabbage. Press the vegetable onto the stamp pad and then onto a
piece   unusual
peace of paper. Different vegetable shapes will make unusal designs.

Level 5   Unit 4 Instructions   *(Use with pupil book pages 133–134.)*
Skill: Students will proofread paragraphs of instructions, correcting mistakes in spelling, capitalization, punctuation, formation of plurals, and paragraph format.

2 | Direct Objects

> The students helped the **astronomers**. (helped whom?)
> Astronomers examine the **stars**. (examine what?)
> They observe **them** with telescopes. (observe what?)

A. Underline the action verb in each sentence. Write the direct object.

1. Maria Mitchell studied the stars. — stars
2. As a child, she helped her father with his work. — father
3. Her father encouraged his daughter. — daughter
4. At the age of twelve, she observed an eclipse. — eclipse
5. After that she increased her knowledge. — knowledge
6. She watched the sky at night through a telescope. — sky
7. She read many books about astronomy. — books
8. In 1847 Maria Mitchell discovered a comet. — comet
9. She gained fame through this discovery. — fame
10. The King of Denmark honored Mitchell. — Mitchell
11. She won a gold medal. — medal
12. The American Academy of Arts and Sciences elected her as a member. — her
13. As the first female member, she paved the way for others. — way
14. Vassar College hired the scientist. — scientist
15. She continued her work in astronomy. — work
16. Mitchell taught it as a subject. — it
17. She helped her students with research. — students
18. As a teacher, Mitchell influenced future astronomers. — astronomers

(continued)

---

1 | Action Verbs (continued from page 49)

B. Writing Application: Instructions

Think of something you have made. It might be a painting, a model, or something you cooked. Write five sentences telling how you made it. Use an action verb in each sentence. Underline the action verbs.

Students to respond on separate paper. Answers will vary.

★ Enrichment ★

The winner of each ticktacktoe game wrote three action verbs in a row. Find out who won each game. First, underline the action verbs in each game. Then write whether "X" or "O" won the game.

Game 1

X cobra	O clean	O continent
X claim	O connect	X county
X cruel	X called	X chariot

1. The winner is O.

Game 2

O restless	O radish	O raisin
O runway	X rotten	O relate
X reacted	X require	X rushed

2. The winner is X.

Game 3

O afloat	O agree	X appreciate
X awkward	O assure	X auditorium
X ankle	X apply	X alphabet

3. The winner is O.

Game 4

O system	X slither	X select
O suggest	X slender	X soar
O surrender	O society	X succeed

4. The winner is X.

Game 5

X freckle	X fact	X forecast
O fade	O freeze	O fled
O full	X fantastic	O fourteen

5. The winner is O.

Game 6

X mineral	X mistaken	O mosquito
O mild	O multiply	O massive
O murmur	X migrate	X mutter

6. The winner is X.

T25

Name _____

LANGUAGE AND USAGE

3 | Main Verbs and Helping Verbs

helping   main
verb   verb
My parents **have left** for the bookstore.

helping main
verb   verb
They **are going** to the annual book sale.

A. Write the verb or the verb phrase in each sentence. For each verb phrase, underline the helping verb once and the main verb twice.

1. Our local bookstore is celebrating Mark Twain's birthday.
is celebrating

2. The store has lowered the prices of all its books.
has lowered

3. Already, sales have broken all records.   **have broken**

4. Yesterday my parents planned their purchases.
planned

5. They are buying many books for gifts.
are buying

6. I am looking for a book by Mark Twain.
am looking

7. However, Mark Twain's books were selling quickly all morning.
were selling

8. Many copies of my favorite books had disappeared by noon.
had disappeared

9. The clerks were piling other books on the tables.
were piling

10. I will get there earlier next year.   **will get**

(continued)

Name _____

LANGUAGE AND USAGE

2 | Direct Objects   (continued from page 51)

B. Writing Application: A Post Card

You have just landed on the moon. Write a post card to a friend, telling what you have found there. Use at least three action verbs and three direct objects. Circle the direct objects.
Students to respond on separate paper. Answers will vary.

★ Enrichment ★

This newspaper story tells about an important discovery. What is it? Explain by completing each sentence below with a direct object.   **Answers will vary.**

NEWS SERVICE NATIONAL 2080:02   7-15

Dr. Carmelita Sanchez discovered a _____ today.

She was working in her laboratory when she suddenly noticed a _____. She grabbed her _____

and checked the _____. First, she dropped

Dr. Sanchez tested the _____ into water. Then she inspected the _____. Nothing had changed. She tried a _____. It didn't work. Finally, she tried _____. It changed the _____.

She had completed her _____.

Her assistants helped _____. They repeated

the _____. They proved the _____.

Officials praise _____. They say that the discovery

aids _____. Dr. Sanchez received a _____ for her accomplishment.

T26

Name _____

LANGUAGE AND USAGE

4 | Linking Verbs

Linking Verbs: Hawaii's nickname **is** the Aloha State.
Hawaii **looks** beautiful.

Action Verbs: The tourist **looks** at the map of Hawaii.
The map **shows** many tourist attractions.

A. Write the verb in each sentence. Label each verb *linking* or *action.*

1. Hawaii is the youngest state in the United States.
is—linking

2. Hawaii's attractions are famous.
are—linking

3. To a visitor, these islands look spectacular.
look—linking

4. The mild climate feels perfect.
feels—linking

5. Visitors feel the warm sun and the cool ocean breezes.
feel—action

6. They enjoy the warm waters of the Pacific Ocean.
enjoy—action

B. Underline the linking verb in each sentence. Draw an arrow showing the words that the verb links.

7. Farm products are a source of income for Hawaiians.

8. Foreign markets seem interested in the islands' many crops.

9. Sugar cane is Hawaii's most important product.

10. Pineapples are its second largest crop.

11. Other fruits appear plentiful on the islands as well.

12. The air smells sweet with the scent of coconuts and bananas.

(continued)

Level 5 Unit 5 Verbs (Use with pupil book pages 148–149.)
Skill: Students will identify action verbs, linking verbs, predicate nouns, and predicate adjectives.

Name _____

LANGUAGE AND USAGE

3 | Main Verbs and Helping Verbs (continued from page 53)

B. Writing Application: Sentences

Write five sentences, telling about a visit that you made to a library or a bookstore. Use a main verb and a helping verb in each sentence. **Students to respond on separate paper. Answers will vary.**

★ Enrichment ★

The first sentence of a story is very important. Read these first sentences. Underline the main verb and the helping verb in each sentence.

"Nothing had gone right that day."

"The mysterious woman and her package had disappeared."

"As usual the twins were arguing with each other."

Now write your own first sentence for each of the stories below. Use a main verb and a helping verb in each sentence. **Answers will vary.**

1. A story about a gas station: _____
2. A story about space travel: _____
3. A story about your school: _____
4. A story about your relatives: _____
5. A story about the future: _____
6. A story about a sports star: _____
7. A story about rock music: _____

Level 5 Unit 5 Verbs (Use with pupil book pages 146–147.)
Skill: Students will use main verbs and helping verbs in sentences.

Name _____

LANGUAGE AND USAGE

5 | Present Tense

George **enjoys** cooking.
He **guesses** the ingredients.
The chef **coaches** George.
Cool air **refreshes** him.
Cooking **relaxes** George.
He **tries** new recipes.

We **enjoy** cooking.
You **guess** the ingredients.
Both chefs **coach** George.
These two fans **refresh** him.
George and the chef **relax**.
I **try** new recipes.

A. Write the correct present tense form of each verb in parentheses.

1. My brother Pete ___**fixes**___ wonderful meals. **(fix)**

2. He ___**takes**___ time and care. **(take)**

3. I ___**watch**___ Pete. **(watch)**

4. He ___**pinches**___ the tomatoes to see if they are ripe. **(pinch)**

5. He ___**washes**___ the lettuce. **(wash)**

6. Then he ___**dries**___ it carefully. **(dry)**

7. He ___**mixes**___ oil and vinegar to make salad dressing. **(mix)**

8. The timer ___**buzzes**___. **(buzz)**

9. My sisters ___**rush**___ into the kitchen. **(rush)**

10. Pete ___**serves**___ the dinner. **(serve)**

11. His stew ___**looks**___ delicious. **(look)**

12. We all ___**enjoy**___ the dinner. **(enjoy)**

13. After dinner we ___**discuss**___ the clean-up duty. **(discuss)**

14. Pete ___**thinks**___ of a number between one and ten. **(think)**

15. We each ___**guess**___ a number. **(guess)**

16. My number ___**comes**___ the closest to Pete's. **(come)**

17. "You ___**win**___!" my sisters shout gleefully. **(win)**

18. I ___**begin**___ to clear the dirty dishes. **(begin)**

(continued)

Level 5   Unit 5 Verbs   *(Use with pupil book pages 150–151.)*
Skill: Students will use present tense verbs correctly with singular and plural subjects.

Name _____

LANGUAGE AND USAGE

4 | Linking Verbs *(continued from page 55)*

C. Writing Application: A Description

Write five sentences, describing your state, province, or city. Use a linking verb from the box below in each sentence.

am	is	are	was	were	will be
look	feel	taste	smell	seem	appear

Students to respond on separate paper. Answers will vary.

★ **Enrichment** ★

Pretend that you are visiting the imaginary tropical island of Tralala. Complete the following sentences about the island. Write a linking verb in each box. Then add words that name or describe the subject of the sentence.

Answers will vary.

1. The climate of this island ☐ _____

2. The flowers here ☐ _____

3. The animals on the island ☐ _____

4. Strange fruits ☐ _____

5. Several bubbling streams ☐ _____

6. The people on this island ☐ _____

7. A huge bird ☐ _____

Level 5   Unit 5 Verbs   *(Use with pupil book pages 148–149.)*
Skill: Students will use linking verbs in sentences.

6 | Past Tense

Eric **watched** the workers.
He **saved** his questions for later.
The workers **stayed** for a long time.
Then they **hurried** to the next job.
They **scrubbed** the kettles thoroughly.

A. Complete each sentence by writing the past tense form of the verb in parentheses.

1. Eric **enjoyed** _____ his visit to Williamsburg. (**enjoy**)

2. He **learned** _____ about the colonists. (**learn**)

3. He **observed** _____ some of the colonists' crafts. (**observe**)

4. The colonists **produced** _____ their own soap. (**produce**)

5. Women **collected** _____ wood ashes from their fireplaces. (**collect**)

6. Their cooking **supplied** _____ fats and grease. (**supply**)

7. The women **carried** _____ the ashes to a large barrel. (**carry**)

8. They **poured** _____ water through the ashes in the barrel. (**pour**)

9. It **dripped** _____ out through a hole near the bottom. (**drip**)

10. The ashes **caused** _____ the water to turn brown. (**cause**)

11. The brown liquid **dropped** _____ into a pail. (**drop**)

12. People **called** _____ this liquid lye. (**call**)

13. The women **placed** _____ the lye in a kettle. (**place**)

14. They **added** _____ the fats and the grease. (**add**)

15. The mixture **boiled** _____ slowly. (**boil**)

16. After a while, the mixture **turned** _____ into a jelly. (**turn**)

17. People **stored** _____ this jellylike substance. (**store**)

18. They **used** _____ the soft and smelly substance for soap. (**use**)

(continued)

---

5 | Present Tense (continued from page 57)

B. Writing Application: A Progress Report

The Parents' Association has hired the students in your class to prepare a special luncheon. Students are busy preparing the food, setting up the room, and putting up decorations. You are in charge of the event. Write a progress report for the Parents' Association. Use the present tense form of five verbs from the box below.

arrange	push	carry	toss	fix	scrub	reach	make

Students to respond on separate paper. Answers will vary.

★ Enrichment ★

Classroom Cookery, a television show, is captioned for people who have difficulty hearing. Below are scenes from four different shows. Explain what is happening in each scene by completing the caption below each picture. Use a verb in the present tense form in each sentence.

1. Cecil and Ron **Answers will vary.**

2. He _____

3. Ming Chen _____

4. The girls _____

T29

Name _____

LANGUAGE AND USAGE

WORKBOOK PLUS ▲ 61

7 ║ Future Tense

> We **shall stay** here this summer.
> My brother **will work** next July.

A. Underline the verb or verb phrase in each sentence. Then rewrite each sentence, using the future tense form of the underlined verb.

1. This summer Eva has traveled to New Mexico.
   This summer Eva will travel to New Mexico.

2. Each year she visits her Aunt Nina, who is a scientist.
   Each year she will visit her Aunt Nina, who is a scientist.

3. Eva helps with the research.
   Eva will help with the research.

4. They work at a large pueblo ruin.
   They will work at a large pueblo ruin.

5. They have traced the development of the pueblo.
   They will trace the development of the pueblo.

6. The scientists have used the latest research techniques.
   The scientists will use the latest research techniques.

7. Their findings have provided information about the Mimbres people.
   Their findings will provide information about the Mimbres people.

8. Aunt Nina and Eva dig with care.
   Aunt Nina and Eva will dig with care.

9. They search for Mimbres pottery.
   They will search for Mimbres pottery.

10. Eva has learned much about archaeology.
    Eva will learn much about archaeology.

Level 5 Unit 5 Verbs   (Use with pupil book pages 154–155.)
Skill: Students will write the future tense forms of verbs.

(continued)

Name _____

LANGUAGE AND USAGE

WORKBOOK PLUS ▲ 60

6 ║ Past Tense   *(continued from page 59)*

B. Writing Application: A Paragraph

A time machine has taken you back to the time of the North American colonists. Now you have returned to the present. Write a paragraph, telling your friends about what you saw. Use at least five past tense verbs. Circle the verbs. Students to respond on separate paper. **Answers will vary.**

★ Enrichment ★

The year is 2588. You have just returned from a time-machine trip back to 1988. While you were on your trip, you took pictures of the machines that people used in 1988. Explain how the people used these machines. Write a sentence for each picture. Use a different past tense verb in each sentence.

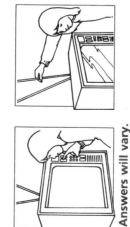  

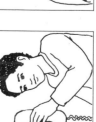  

Answers will vary.

Level 5 Unit 5 Verbs   (Use with pupil book pages 152–153.)
Skill: Students will write the past tense forms of regular verbs.

UNIT 5 TEACHER'S ANNOTATED PAGES

T30

LANGUAGE AND USAGE

7 | Future Tense *(continued from page 61)*

B. Writing Application: A Paragraph

Write a paragraph, describing your plans for next summer. Your plans can be real or imaginary. Use a future tense verb in each sentence. Underline each verb. **Students to respond on separate paper. Answers will vary.**

Enrichment

The symbols below are taken from an ancient Egyptian form of writing called hieroglyphics. Scientists often find this kind of writing in Egyptian ruins. Use the meanings of the symbols to write a sentence for each group of symbols below. Use a future tense verb in each sentence. Sample answers:

person	see	woods, tree	write
cut, knife	plants	buildings	animals
foreign country	water	go, walk	books, paintings
eat, speak	food	boat, sail	steps, climb

1. **The person will write a book.**

2. **The person will go to a foreign country.**

3. **The person will see buildings.**

4. **The animals will see plants.**

5. **The person will eat food.**

6. **Animals will eat plants.**

Now draw two hieroglyphic sentences of your own. Then write each sentence, using a future tense verb.

7. **Answers will vary.**

8. _____

Level 5   Unit 5 Verbs   *(Use with pupil book pages 154–155.)*
Skill: Students will write the future tense forms of verbs.

LANGUAGE AND USAGE

8 | Subject-Verb Agreement

Singular Subjects	Plural Subjects	I or you
Cleo **rides** the bus.	The girls **ride** the bus.	You **ride** the bus.
She **enjoys** the ride.	We **enjoy** the ride.	I **enjoy** the ride.
My brother **catches** the bus.	Cleo and I **catch** the bus.	You **catch** the bus.

A. Rewrite each sentence, using the correct present tense form of the verb in parentheses.

1. My brother ___?___ for the government. (work)
   My brother works for the government.

2. He ___?___ public transportation. (plan)
   He plans public transportation.

3. Public transportation ___?___ trains, subways, and buses. (include)
   Public transportation includes trains, subways, and buses.

4. It ___?___ people and the environment. (help)
   It helps people and the environment.

5. My brother and I ___?___ problems in public transportation. (discuss)
   My brother and I discuss problems in public transportation.

6. We ___?___ about the increase in automobile traffic. (talk)
   We talk about the increase in automobile traffic.

7. The roads ___?___ more crowded each year. (become)
   The roads become more crowded each year.

8. My brother and other workers ___?___ different solutions. (try)
   My brother and other workers try different solutions.

9. They ___?___ the use of public transportation. (encourage)
   They encourage the use of public transportation.

10. Now I ___?___ the bus whenever possible. (ride)
    Now I ride the bus whenever possible.

(continued)

Level 5   Unit 5 Verbs   *(Use with pupil book pages 156–157.)*
Skill: Students will write verbs that agree with singular and plural subjects.

Name _____

LANGUAGE AND USAGE

9 | Agreement with be and have

Subjects	Forms of be	Forms of have
I	am, was	have, had
he, she, it	is, was	has, had
singular nouns	is, was	has, had
you, we, they	are, were	have, had
plural nouns	are, were	have, had

A. The underlined verb in each sentence does not agree with its subject. Rewrite each sentence correctly.

1. Has you ever built a model airplane?
   Have you ever built a model airplane?

2. I is building one now.
   I am building one now.

3. It are a free-flight model with no wires.
   It is a free-flight model with no wires.

4. Most free-flight models is made from balsa wood.
   Most free-flight models are made from balsa wood.

5. This model have a wingspan of six feet.
   This model has a wingspan of six feet.

6. Grandfather have given me advice on it.
   Grandfather has given me advice on it.

7. He were once an airline pilot.
   He was once an airline pilot.

8. We was planning to use a piston engine for power.
   We were planning to use a piston engine for power.

9. Grandfather and I is entering an air show this year.
   Grandfather and I are entering an air show this year.

10. I were too young to enter last year.
    I was too young to enter last year.

(continued)

Name _____

LANGUAGE AND USAGE

8 | Subject-Verb Agreement   *(continued from page 63)*

B. **Writing Application: A Travel Diary**

You and a friend are taking a trip by bus, car, or train. Write at least five sentences for your diary, telling about what happens on the journey. Use the present tense form of a verb in each sentence. Make sure each verb agrees with its subject.
Students to respond on separate paper. Answers will vary.

★ Enrichment ★

Read the bus schedule below and answer the questions that follow. Each answer should be a complete sentence that uses a verb in the present tense form. Try to use a different subject for each sentence.

	COBURN	TYVILLE	**ARRIVES** MAXTON	SIMPSON	JEROME
LEAVES	9:30 A.M.	10:00 A.M.	10:10 A.M.	10:15 A.M.	10:20 A.M.
	11:00 A.M.	11:30 A.M.	11:40 A.M.	11:45 A.M.	11:50 A.M.
	1:30 P.M.	2:00 P.M.	2:10 P.M.	2:15 P.M.	2:20 P.M.

Sample answers:

1. When does the first bus leave Coburn in the morning?
   It leaves at 9:30 A.M.

2. When does the 1:30 P.M. bus arrive in Tyville?
   The bus arrives at 2:00 P.M.

3. What time do I get to Maxton if I take the 11:00 A.M. bus?
   You get there at 11:40 A.M.

4. Which two stops come between Tyville and Jerome?
   Maxton and Simpson come between Tyville and Jerome.

5. What do people call the last stop on the line?
   They call it Jerome.

6. How do I get to Simpson before 10:30 A.M.?
   You take the 9:30 A.M. bus from Coburn.

LANGUAGE AND USAGE

10 | Contractions with *not*

Verb + *not*	Contraction	Verb + *not*	Contraction
do not	don't	has not	hasn't
did not	didn't	had not	hadn't
is not	isn't	would not	wouldn't
were not	weren't	cannot	can't
will not	won't	must not	mustn't

A. Write the contraction for each underlined word or words.

1. Max, I <u>cannot</u> go to the concert with you. _____ can't

2. <u>Are you not</u> feeling well? _____ Aren't

3. I <u>do not</u> have my science report finished yet. _____ don't

4. Dad <u>will not</u> let me go until it is done. _____ won't

5. The report is <u>not</u> due until next week. _____ isn't

6. I <u>could not</u> work on it over the weekend. _____ couldn't

7. It <u>has not</u> even been started yet! _____ hasn't

8. I <u>had not</u> done my research until this week. _____ hadn't

9. I <u>did not</u> know it would take this much time. _____ didn't

B. Write the words that were combined to form the contraction in each sentence.

10. I wasn't the only person going with you, I hope. _____ was not

11. No, you weren't. Josh is coming too. _____ were not

12. Well, that doesn't seem so bad. _____ does not

13. I wouldn't want to spoil your fun. _____ would not

14. You mustn't worry about that. _____ must not

15. A concert shouldn't interfere with your schoolwork. _____ should not

16. I didn't want to ruin everything. _____ did not

17. You haven't, but I wish you could go. _____ have not

18. Next time I won't wait until the last minute. _____ will not

(continued)

Level 5 Unit 5 Verbs   *(Use with pupil book pages 160–161.)*
Skill: Students will identify and will write contractions.

LANGUAGE AND USAGE

9 | Agreement with *be* and *have*   (continued from page 65)

B. **Writing Application: Creative Writing**

Imagine that you are so small that you can fit into a model plane. Write a paragraph about a trip you take. Use forms of *be* and *have* in your sentences. Make sure that the verbs agree with their subjects.

Students to respond on separate paper. Answers will vary.

★ Enrichment ★

Captain Chang's plane has encountered rough weather. She has radioed for help, but static has made parts of the air traffic controller's answer impossible to understand. Help Captain Chang by rewriting the answer. Use a form of *be* or *have* wherever you run into static!

Roger, Flight 555. We ⋀⋀⋀ you on radar. We ⋀⋀⋀ reading you, and your request ⋀⋀⋀ been received. The weather you ⋀⋀⋀ experiencing ⋀⋀⋀ a low-pressure area stretching from Springdale to Winter Valley. The storm ⋀⋀⋀ moving at twenty-five miles per hour due east. You ⋀⋀⋀ passed the center of the storm and ⋀⋀⋀ out of danger. We ⋀⋀⋀ routing you through Summerville, however, because another storm front ⋀⋀⋀ approached from the north. At present your altitude ⋀⋀⋀ holding steady. It looks as if the worst ⋀⋀⋀ over. We ⋀⋀⋀ transferred you to air traffic control at Summerville. Good luck. Over.

Roger, Flight 555. We have you on radar. We are reading you, and your request has been received. The weather you are experiencing is a low-pressure area stretching from Springdale to Winter Valley. The storm is moving at twenty-five miles per hour due east. You have passed the center of the storm and are out of danger. We are routing you through Summerville, however, because another storm front has approached from the north. At present your altitude is holding steady. It looks as if the worst is over. We have transferred you to air traffic control at Summerville. Good luck. Over.

Level 5 Unit 5 Verbs   *(Use with pupil book pages 158–159.)*
Skill: Students will write forms of *be* and *have* that agree with singular and plural subjects.

Name _____

11 | Regular and Irregular Verbs

	Verb	Past Tense	Past with Helping Verb
Regular Verbs:	paint	painted	(has, have, had) painted
	hire	hired	(has, have, had) hired
	spy	spied	(has, have, had) spied
Irregular Verbs:	go	went	(has, have, had) gone
	think	thought	(has, have, had) thought

A. In the first column, write the past tense form of each underlined verb. In the second column, write the past form of the verb when it is used with a helping verb.

1. We start a class newspaper.   started   have started
2. We go to the newspaper office.   went   had gone
3. We come back with good ideas.   came   had come
4. We try them out.   tried   have tried
5. Eduardo brings his camera.   brought   has brought
6. He uses it a lot.   used   has used
7. He takes good pictures.   took   has taken
8. He makes copies of the photographs.   made   has made
9. He wants a career as a photographer.   wanted   had wanted
10. He says so to his friends.   said   has said
11. Doreen thinks differently.   thought   has thought
12. She hopes to be a writer.   hoped   had hoped
13. She always carries a pad with her.   carried   had carried
14. She writes articles for the paper.   wrote   has written
15. Several of her articles run in it.   ran   have run
16. Eduardo and Doreen cover sports.   covered   have covered
17. They report on every game.   reported   have reported
18. Doreen interviews the players.   interviewed   had interviewed

(continued)

Level 5 Unit 5 Verbs   *(Use with pupil book pages 162–163.)*
Skill: Students will write the past and past participle forms of regular and irregular verbs.

Name _____

10 | Contractions with *not*   *(continued from page 67)*

C. Writing Application: A Letter

You were supposed to go somewhere with a friend, and now you find that you are unable to go. Write a letter of apology, explaining what has happened. Include at least five contractions that use the word *not*.
Students to respond on separate paper. Answers will vary.

★ Enrichment ★

You are writing a science report on safety. Write two sentences that tell about each picture set. In the first sentence, tell what to do. In the second sentence, tell what not to do. Use a different contraction in the second sentence of each pair.
Sample answers:

YES   NO

1. A bicycle should carry only one person. A bicycle shouldn't carry more than one person.

2. Put your toys away. Leaving toys out isn't safe.

3. You should stop and look before going into the street. You mustn't run into the street.

4. Use safe electrical cords. Old electrical cords aren't safe.

Level 5 Unit 5 Verbs   *(Use with pupil book pages 160–161.)*
Skill: Students will use contractions in sentences.

T34

LANGUAGE AND USAGE

12 | More Irregular Verbs

Verb	Past Tense	Past with Helping Verb
sing	sang	(has, have, had) sung
begin	began	(has, have, had) begun
wear	wore	(has, have, had) worn
choose	chose	(has, have, had) chosen
grow	grew	(has, have, had) grown

A. Rewrite each sentence. Use the correct past form of the verb in parentheses.

1. Ivan __?__ a glance at the thermometer. (steal)
   Ivan stole a glance at the thermometer.

2. He had __?__ winter was coming. (know)
   He had known winter was coming.

3. It __?__ with the first cold spell. (begin)
   It began with the first cold spell.

4. That morning in October, he had __?__ in the pond. (swim)
   That morning in October, he had swum in the pond.

5. In the afternoon, it had __?__ cold. (grow)
   In the afternoon, it had grown cold.

6. Ivan __?__ a sweater for the first time in months. (wear)
   Ivan wore a sweater for the first time in months.

7. Since then the water in the pond has __?__. (freeze)
   Since then the water in the pond has frozen.

8. The wind has __?__ the leaves from the trees. (blow)
   The wind has blown the leaves from the trees.

9. Many of the birds __?__ south weeks ago. (fly)
   Many of the birds flew south weeks ago.

10. Only the cardinals and the blue jays have __?__ to stay. (choose)
    Only the cardinals and the blue jays have chosen to stay.

(continued)

LANGUAGE AND USAGE

11 | Regular and Irregular Verbs *(continued from page 69)*

B. Writing Application: A Job Application

You are applying for a job as either a newspaper photographer or reporter. Write five sentences about pictures that you have taken or articles that you have written. Use past forms of five of the verbs from the box below.

> bring   come   go   make   say   take   think   write

Students to respond on separate paper. Answers will vary.

Enrichment

Nina Newsworthy is interviewing two candidates for class president. Help Nina finish her interview. Complete each candidate's answers. Use a past form of a verb from the box in each of your answers.

> run   bring   come   go   make   say   take   think   write

Sample answers:

Nina: What schools have you attended in the past?

Candidate 1: I have **gone to Park School since first grade** .

Candidate 2: I **came here from a school in Houston last year** .

Nina: Have you ever run for a class office before?

Candidate 1: I have **run for class secretary before** .

Candidate 2: I **ran for president in the fourth grade** .

Nina: What class projects have you been involved in?

Candidate 1: I **made posters for the craft sale** .

Candidate 2: I have **taken pictures for the class newspaper** .

Nina: What do you think the class has accomplished in the past year?

Candidate 1: The class **brought interesting guest speakers to the school** .

Candidate 2: We have **written a class constitution** .

Nina: What should be the class's major concern for next year?

Candidate 1: I **thought we should raise money for a class trip** .

Candidate 2: I have **said that community service is most important** .

Page 72

Name _____

12 ▌ More Irregular Verbs   *(continued from page 71)*

B. Writing Application: Sentences

Write five sentences about how you once knew that spring was coming. In each sentence, use a past form of one of the verbs from the box below.

sing	begin	blow	know
swim	wear	grow	fly

Students to respond on separate paper. Answers will vary.

★ **Enrichment** ★

Write six alphabet sentences. Use a past form of a verb from the box below. Then write a sentence, using words that begin with the same letter as the verb. Each sentence must have at least four words. The first sentence has been done for you.

ring	begin	break	freeze	fly
swim	wear	choose	grow	tear

1. Five flocks of feathered finch had flown from the forest.

2. **Answers will vary.** _____

3. _____

4. _____

5. _____

6. _____

Page 73

Name _____

13 ▌ Verb Phrases with *have*

Verb Phrases	Verb Phrases with Contractions
I **could have tried** to go.	I **could've tried** to go.
You **would have enjoyed** the day.	You **would've enjoyed** the day.
We **should have packed** a picnic.	We **should've packed** a picnic.
She **must have seen** the float.	She **must've seen** the float.

A. Rewrite the verb phrase in each sentence so that it includes a contraction.

1. You should have seen that parade!   **should've seen**

2. I could have gotten there earlier.   **could've gotten**

3. It must have been a good one.   **must've been**

4. I could have left my house earlier.   **could've left**

5. I should have remembered the time.   **should've remembered**

6. You would have liked our float.   **would've liked**

7. I could have taken a picture of it for you.   **could've taken**

8. People must have come from miles away.   **must've come**

9. The children would have watched the show all day.   **would've watched**

10. They must have stayed for at least two hours.   **must've stayed**

B. Write the verb phrase in each sentence so that it does not include a contraction. If the verb phrase is incorrect, write it correctly.

11. You should've seen my mother in the band.   **should have seen**

12. Her music would of amazed you.   **would have amazed**

13. She must've practiced for months.   **must have practiced**

14. She could of passed for a professional musician.   **could have passed**

15. The band should've had more time.   **should have had**

16. They must of been the best act in the parade.   **must have been**

(continued)

Page 74

Name _____

LANGUAGE AND USAGE

13 | Verb Phrases with *have*   (continued *from page 73*)

C. Writing Application: Sentences

Imagine that you were once a clown in a parade. Write six sentences about your act. Use a different verb phrase with *have* in each sentence.

Students to respond on separate paper. Answers will vary.

★ Enrichment ★

The members of the Nature Club are having problems making their float. Help them by writing a solution to each problem shown in the pictures below. Try to use a different verb phrase with *have* or *'ve* in each sentence.

Sample answers:

He should've used less glue.

Libby could've stopped making flowers earlier.

A different head for the zebra would've helped.

They should have turned the banner around.

Level 5   Unit 5   Verbs   *(Use with pupil book pages 166–167.)*
Skill: Students will write verb phrases with *have.*

Page 75

Name _____

LANGUAGE AND USAGE

14 | *teach, learn; let, leave*

Will you **teach** me about camps?
I would like to **learn** how to find a good one.
Will your mother **let** you go?
She said I could **leave** for camp next summer.
I must **leave** my dog at home.

A. Complete each sentence with the correct word in parentheses.

1. Mr. Berg will ___teach___ us about camping.   (teach, learn)
2. Students will ___learn___ about many kinds of camps.   (teach, learn)
3. Leaders ___teach___ the campers many useful things.   (teach, learn)
4. They ___let___ the campers work independently.   (let, leave)
5. Campers ___learn___ to do things on their own.   (teach, learn)
6. Some campers ___leave___ home in the summer.   (let, leave)
7. Their parents ___let___ them go to overnight camp.   (let, leave)
8. They ___leave___ their families behind.   (let, leave)
9. At camp they ___learn___ how to live outdoors.   (teach, learn)
10. Eric will ___leave___ for camp next July.   (let, leave)
11. His parents will ___let___ him go for two weeks.   (let, leave)
12. His sister will ___let___ him borrow her camera.   (let, leave)
13. A volunteer will ___teach___ him to take pictures.   (teach, learn)
14. Eric will ___learn___ other skills too.   (teach, learn)
15. The staff will ___teach___ him to swim and to sail.   (teach, learn)
16. Eric's brother will ___let___ him use his sleeping bag.   (let, leave)
17. Eric hates to ___leave___ his relatives at home.   (let, leave)
18. However, he will ___learn___ a lot at camp.   (teach, learn)

(continued)

Level 5   Unit 5   Verbs   *(Use with pupil book pages 168–169.)*
Skill: Students will use *teach, learn, let,* and *leave* correctly.

Name _____

15 | sit, set; can, may

I **sit** in a big, comfortable chair.
I **set** my appointment card on the front desk.
I **can** hear the dentist's drill.
May I go home now?

A. One verb in each sentence is used incorrectly. Rewrite each sentence correctly.

1. Please set in the waiting room until the dentist is ready.
Please sit in the waiting room until the dentist is ready.

2. You can come in now.
You may come in now.

3. Set in the large chair by the sink.
Sit in the large chair by the sink.

4. Sit your books on the table by the window.
Set your books on the table by the window.

5. May you lean back a little farther?
Can you lean back a little farther?

6. May you feel the cavity in that molar?
Can you feel the cavity in that molar?

7. You'll have to sit a date to have it filled.
You'll have to set a date to have it filled.

8. Can I finish cleaning your teeth now?
May I finish cleaning your teeth now?

9. You can rinse out your mouth now.
You may rinse out your mouth now.

10. You may set up now that we're finished.
You may sit up now that we're finished.

Level 5 Unit 5 Verbs (Use with pupil book pages 170–171.)
Skill: Students will use sit, set, can, and may correctly.

(continued)

Name _____

14 | teach, learn; let, leave (continued from page 75)

B. Writing Application: A Letter

Pretend that you are at summer camp. Write a letter to your relatives at home. Tell them what you are doing. Use the verbs *teach, learn, let,* and *leave.*
Students to respond on separate paper. Answers will vary.

★ Enrichment ★

It is visiting day at camp. Use the map below to answer the visitors' questions. Write a complete sentence for each answer. Use the words *teach, learn, let,* and *leave* in your answers.

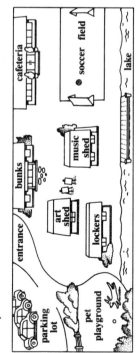

1. Where do I park my car?
Leave your car in the parking lot.

2. Where can my dog run?
Let your dog off the leash in the pet playground.

3. Where can we sing the new camp song?
Learn the camp song in the music shed.

4. Where can I watch the coach instructing the soccer team?
Watch the soccer coach teach the campers on the soccer field.

Now write one more question a visitor might ask. Then write your answer, using the verb *teach, learn, let,* or *leave.*

5. _____
Answers will vary.

Level 5 Unit 5 Verbs (Use with pupil book pages 168–169.)
Skill: Students will use teach, learn, let, and leave correctly.

COMPOSITION SKILL: STORY

Plot

There are three main parts to a **plot**. The **beginning** starts with a problem. The **middle** tells what happens as a result of the opening situation. The **end** tells how the problem and its resulting complications are solved.

Think of a story you have read. Write a plot outline of the story. Write only the main points of each part. Leave out the details.

Beginning: _____Answers will vary._____

_____

_____

_____

Middle: _____

_____

_____

_____

_____

End: _____

_____

_____

Level 5 Unit 6 Story *(Use with pupil book page 205.)*
Skill: Students will write the plot outline of a story, including the main points of the beginning, the middle, and the end.

LANGUAGE AND USAGE

15 | *sit, set; can, may* (continued from page 77)

B. Writing Application: Instructions

Write six instructions a dentist might give you for taking care of your teeth. Include the verbs *sit, set, can,* and *may* in your instructions. **Students to respond on separate paper. Answers will vary.**

★ Enrichment ★

The inventors of the machines below thought that their inventions would help people take care of their teeth. The only problem was that no one could figure out how to use them. Write two sentences of instructions for each invention. Use the verb *sit, set, can,* or *may* in each sentence.

Answers will vary.

1. Max Grogl invented a switch that turns off the dentist's drill when the patient wants to say "ouch."

_____

_____

2. Martina Vesper invented the combination toothbrush-radio that makes brushing your teeth more fun.

_____

_____

Now draw your own dental invention. Write two sentences that tell about it.

_____

_____

Level 5 Unit 5 Verbs *(Use with pupil book pages 170–171.)*
Skill: Students will use *sit, set, can,* and *may* correctly.

T39

Name _____

COMPOSITION SKILL: STORY

Setting and Characters (continued from page 80)

C. Choose one of the story settings that you described on page 89. Then think about two characters who might appear in a story with that setting. Describe each character by writing two sentences to answer each question below.

Character 1:

1. What does Character 1 think and do? **Answers will vary.**

_____
_____

2. What does Character 1 tell about Character 2?

_____
_____

Answers will vary.

Character 2:

3. What does Character 2 think and do? **Answers will vary.**

_____
_____

4. What does Character 2 tell about Character 1?

_____
_____

D. Now write a dialogue between your two characters. Write at least four sentences. Show what each character is like by what each one says.
Answers will vary.

_____
_____
_____
_____
_____
_____
_____

Level 5   Unit 6   Story   (Use with pupil book pages 206–207.)
Skill: Students will use different methods to tell what story characters are like.

Name _____

COMPOSITION SKILL: STORY

Setting and Characters

The **setting** is the time and the place of a story. The **characters** are the people, the animals, or the imaginary creatures in a story.

A. Choose one of the story settings below. Write five sentences that show rather than tell about the setting.

1. Inside the world's tallest building just after it is completed
2. A cattle ranch in the Southwest during the hottest part of the year
3. A big city, one hundred years from now
4. A school playground on the first day of the school year

Answers will vary.

_____
_____
_____
_____
_____

B. Think of your own setting for a story. Write at least five sentences that show rather than tell about the setting.
Answers will vary.

_____
_____
_____
_____
_____

(continued)

Level 5   Unit 6   Story   (Use with pupil book pages 206–207.)
Skill: Students will write sentences that show two settings for stories.

T40

Step 3: Revise

Have I   yes

checked that the story has a plot and added to the middle so
the plot makes sense?   ☐

added details to help describe the setting?   ☐

added dialogue to show what the characters are like?   ☐

changed the tenses of some verbs so that all verbs are in the
same tense?   ☐

Revise the following story. Use the check list above to help you. Check off each
box when you have finished your revision.

• Use the space above each line, on the sides, and below the story for your
changes.

Sample answers:

The Case of the Missing Bicycle

~~Once upon a time,~~ Ten-year-old Detective Jones was sitting in

Papers were everywhere. Stale sandwiches sat in a corner. **Suddenly**
his messy office.~~when~~ a little boy burst through the door. He
                    was
had a problem. He ~~is~~ very upset.   "**Please, Detective Jones, you have to**

help me!" cried Tommy. "My brand-new bicycle is missing. I don't know where it is!"
~~Detective Jones calmed him down. He talked to the little~~
☐ "Now, calm down," said Jones. "Tell me all about it."
~~boy.~~ He listened very carefully. He took notes in a little black
                                                       set off outdoors to look
book. Then Detective Jones ~~looked~~ for clues. ~~He found some.~~
            Detective Jones brought the bicycle to Tommy's house.
~~Then he found the bicycle in an old shack.~~ Tommy ~~is~~ (was)
                                                            said
He said, "Detective Jones, you get the job done!"
happy. ∧ Detective Jones ~~is~~ pleased.
              (was)

"Another case solved, another client satisfied," he ~~says~~ as
                                                     said
returned
he ~~returns~~ to his office.

⎡ He went to where Tommy had last seen his bicycle. He found tire tracks. He ⎤
⎣ followed them to an old shack. He looked inside. There was Tommy's bike. ⎦

Level 5   Unit 6   Story   (Use with pupil book pages 211–212.)
Skill: Students will revise a story, checking that the story has a plot, adding to the middle, adding details and
          dialogue, and making verb tenses consistent.

Step 4: Proofread

Proofreading Marks

ꟼ Indent.
∧ Add something.
ℐ Take out something.
≡ Capitalize.
/ Make a small letter.

should've tried
i ~~should of tryed~~ harder.
                ≡

Proofread the following paragraphs. There are three spelling errors, four punctuation errors, two run-on sentences,
and two mistakes in paragraph format. There are also four
errors in capitalization and three errors in forming contractions. Use proofreading marks to correct the mistakes. Use
a dictionary to check your spelling.

                                children
Mr. and Mrs. Hall decided that their ~~chidren~~, Anna and Georgie, needed a pet.
                                                                   could've
The family went to a pet store and looked at different animals.~~They could of~~
                                                          carried
selected a dog or a cat, but they didn't. Instead, they ~~carryed~~ home a strange bird.it
                                                                                        ≡
was a foot tall and had three fuzzy blue feathers on its head, a big orange beak, and
              finally
green wings. ~~they finnaly~~ named it Harold. ꟼHarold could do many amazing
              ≡
tricks. He knew words in seven languages.He could also turn on the radio with his

beak, and he loved to swoop down and pick up objects off the ground. ꟼSoon

strange things began to happen. One of ~~anna~~'s friends said a shrill voice speaking
                                         ≡
~~japanese~~ had been answering the Halls' telephone. Then the police called.they said
  ≡
neighbors had complained about loud music coming from the apartment during the

day. Something had to be done.
        should've
"We ~~should of~~ gotten a big cage for Harold," sighed Mrs. ~~hall~~.
                                                              ≡

Level 5   Unit 6   Story   (Use with pupil book pages 213–214.)
Skill: Students will proofread paragraphs from a story, correcting mistakes in spelling, capitalization,
          punctuation, paragraph format, and the formation of contractions.

Name _____

LANGUAGE AND USAGE

1 | **What Is an Adjective?** *(continued from page 85)*

B. Writing Application: A Description

You and your family are moving to a new country. Imagine what your new home will be like. Write at least five sentences, describing your new home. Use two adjectives in each sentence.

Students to respond on separate paper. Answers will vary.

★ **Enrichment** ★

Printed below are the words *The Statue of Liberty*. On the line next to each letter, write a group of words consisting of one noun or pronoun and at least two adjectives. Every word should begin with the letter at the beginning of the line. The first one has been done for you.

T   **twelve timid travelers**

H   **Answers will vary.**

E   _____

S   _____

T   _____

A   _____

T   _____

U   _____

E   _____

O   _____

F   _____

L   _____

I   _____

B   _____

E   _____

R   _____

T   _____

Y   _____

Level 5 Unit 7 Adjectives *(Use with pupil book pages 222–223.)*
Skill: Students will use adjectives in sentences and in phrases.

Name _____

LANGUAGE AND USAGE

1 | **What Is an Adjective?**

> **What Kind:** **Nervous, impatient** travelers stood at the rail.
> They were **weary** and **hungry**.
>
> **How Many:** **Many** immigrants had come before them.

A. Write each adjective and the noun or the pronoun that it describes. Do not include *a, an,* or *the.*

1. A single ship moved toward the bustling harbor.
   single—ship, bustling—harbor

2. It was noisy and crowded.
   noisy—It, crowded—It

3. Many adults were happy and talkative.
   Many—adults, happy—adults, talkative—adults

4. They were eager to reach the final destination.
   eager—They, final—destination

5. Two small girls peered toward the distant land.
   Two—girls, small—girls, distant—land

6. They were curious about the future.
   curious—They

7. Would they like living in the large, strange country?
   large—country, strange—country

8. Suddenly they heard several joyous shouts.
   several—shouts, joyous—shouts

9. An enormous, majestic statue appeared on the horizon.
   enormous—statue, majestic—statue

10. The brilliant torch welcomed the travelers to a new home.
    brilliant—torch, new—home

(continued)

Level 5 Unit 7 Adjectives *(Use with pupil book pages 222–223.)*
Skill: Students will identify adjectives and the nouns or the pronouns they modify.

T43

LANGUAGE AND USAGE

2 | Articles and Demonstrative Adjectives

Articles: A storm is predicted.
Do you have **an** umbrella or **an** old raincoat?
The rain should begin soon.

Demonstrative Adjectives: **This** forecast is more accurate than **that** one.
These reports are better than **those** reports.

A. Rewrite each sentence, using the correct word in parentheses.

1. (A, An) long time ago, there were no daily weather reports.
   A long time ago, there were no daily weather reports.

2. In (these, those) days, people couldn't predict weather as we can today.
   In those days, people couldn't predict weather as we can today.

3. That age was not as scientific as (this, that) one.
   That age was not as scientific as this one.

4. At (that, this) time, people depended more on natural signs.
   At that time, people depended more on natural signs.

5. Roosting birds were (a, an) indication of rain.
   Roosting birds were an indication of rain.

6. A red sky at night meant that (an, the) next day would be fair.
   A red sky at night meant that the next day would be fair.

7. Red lightning meant that (a, an) storm was approaching.
   Red lightning meant that a storm was approaching.

8. In (those, these) days, weather prediction was less exact than now.
   In those days, weather prediction was less exact than now.

9. However, forecasters still use (these, those) signs of long ago.
   However, forecasters still use those signs of long ago.

10. (A, An) accurate forecast is the product of many different methods.
    An accurate forecast is the product of many different methods.

(continued)

LANGUAGE AND USAGE

2 | Articles and Demonstrative Adjectives (continued from page 87)

B. Writing Application: Sentences

Write five sentences about natural changes that you might notice before a storm.
Use articles and demonstrative adjectives in your sentences.
Students to respond on separate paper. Answers will vary.

★ Enrichment ★

Discover tomorrow's weather forecast. Color the spaces containing nouns that can be used with the article or the demonstrative adjective at the beginning of each row.

the	day	map		sea	snow	rain		wind	sky	ice
an	inn	sky	wind	eagle	day	age	map	ear	sea	clouds
a	city	icicle	eel	winter	ace	frost	egg	storm	ocean	uncle
this	time	night	cities	front	seas	spring	clouds	street	rivers	smog
these	clouds	wind	sea	hills	city	days	age	maps	log	charts
that	ocean	hills	clouds	sea	wind	storms	snow	charts	days	fall
those	days	moon	wind	clouds	tides	bees	sun	storms	charts	maps

Now write seven sentences about the weather. In each sentence, use a different article or demonstrative adjective and one of the nouns that you colored.

Answers will vary.

1. _____
2. _____
3. _____
4. _____
5. _____
6. _____
7. _____

Page 89

Name _____

LANGUAGE AND USAGE

3 Comparing with Adjectives

Adjective	Comparing Two	Comparing Three or More
great	greater	greatest
nice	nicer	nicest
easy	easier	easiest
big	bigger	biggest
important	more important	most important

A. Write the correct form of the adjective in parentheses to complete each sentence.

1. Mozart's story is one of the **strangest** in music. (strange)

2. He was one of the **youngest** composers in the world. (young)

3. He was **more interested** in music than in other subjects. (interested)

4. Few composers had **more thorough** training than Mozart. (thorough)

5. His father was one of the **ablest** of all teachers. (able)

6. Mozart's performances were **more popular** than his compositions. (popular)

7. Yet he became the **most brilliant** composer of his time. (brilliant)

8. Mozart's works are among the **most beautiful** in music. (beautiful)

9. His operas are **funnier** than many other operas. (funny)

10. However, his music was **more cheerful** than his life. (cheerful)

11. Mozart was not the **happiest** person in the world. (happy)

12. Other musicians were **wealthier** than he was. (wealthy)

13. Mozart's last days were the **saddest** days of all. (sad)

14. Mozart's brilliant career was **shorter** than others'. (short)

15. Yet his popularity is **greater** now than ever before. (great)

16. He is one of the **finest** composers of all time. (fine)

(continued)

Level 5   Unit 7   Adjectives   (Use with pupil book pages 226–227.)
Skill: Students will write the comparative and the superlative forms of adjectives.

Page 90

Name _____

LANGUAGE AND USAGE

3 Comparing with Adjectives (continued from page 89)

B. Writing Application: Sentences

Write six sentences, comparing three songs that you know. Use an adjective that compares in each sentence.
Students will respond on separate paper. Answers will vary.

Enrichment

Write an adjective beneath the first box in each row. Beneath the second box, write the form of the adjective that compares two. Beneath the third box, write the form of the adjective that compares three or more. Draw pictures to illustrate the three forms of adjective. An example has been done for you.

ADJECTIVE	COMPARING TWO	COMPARING THREE OR MORE
1. difficult	more difficult	most difficult
2. Answers will vary.		
3.		
4.		

Level 5   Unit 7   Adjectives   (Use with pupil book pages 226–227.)
Skill: Students will write the comparative and the superlative forms of adjectives.

LANGUAGE AND USAGE

4 | Comparing with good and bad

> **Good:** This is a **good** apple.
> This apple is **better** than that one.
> This is the **best** apple I've ever eaten.
>
> **Bad:** This looks like a **bad** pear.
> It looks **worse** than that pear.
> It looks like the **worst** pear in the bunch.

A. Complete each sentence by writing the correct form of *good*.

1. This is the **best** meal I have ever eaten.
2. Yes, Benita is a very **good** cook.
3. She is even **better** than I am.
4. She makes **better** stews than those the restaurant serves.
5. Her salads are very **good** too.
6. Her fruit salads are **better** than her vegetable salads.
7. The meat she serves is the **best** in town.
8. Her roast turkey is the **best** of all.

B. Complete each sentence by writing the correct form of *bad*.

9. The **worst** meal I ever had here was a cheese sandwich.
10. Benita must have been in a very **bad** mood.
11. The sandwich was **worse** than the cafeteria's sandwiches.
12. It was even **worse** than the meals at the diner.
13. It was the **worst** sandwich in the world!
14. How can a cheese sandwich be that **bad**?
15. The bread tasted **worse** than cardboard!
16. Actually, that part wasn't so **bad**.
17. The **worst** part of all was that there was no cheese!
18. A cheese sandwich without cheese is a pretty **bad** sandwich.

(continued)

Level 5 Unit 7 Adjectives (Use with pupil book pages 228–229.)
Skill: Students will use the correct forms of good and bad.

LANGUAGE AND USAGE

4 | Comparing with good and bad (continued from page 91)

C. Writing Application: Comparison and Contrast

Pretend that you have a job inspecting school cafeterias. Write a paragraph, comparing three meals that you have eaten in your school cafeteria. Use the adjectives *good, better, best, bad, worse,* and *worst* in your paragraph. **Students to respond on separate paper. Answers will vary.**

Enrichment

Henrietta reviews restaurants for a newspaper. You can help Henrietta write her next review. Think of a restaurant you know. Fill in the blanks labeled *adjective* with forms of *good* or *bad*. Follow the directions for filling in the other blanks.

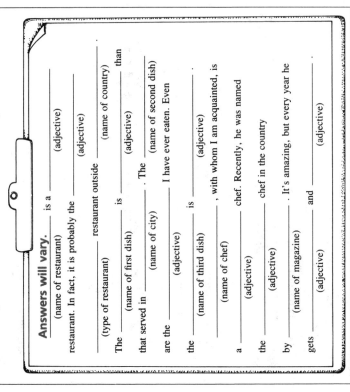

Answers will vary.

_____ is a _____ (adjective) restaurant. In fact, it is probably the _____ (adjective)
(name of restaurant)

_____ restaurant outside _____ .
(type of restaurant)   (name of country)

The _____ is _____ than _____ . The _____
(name of first dish) (adjective)   (name of city)   (name of second dish)

are the _____ . I have ever eaten. Even the _____ is _____ ,
(adjective)   (name of third dish) (adjective)

_____ , with whom I am acquainted, is a _____ chef. Recently, he was named
(name of chef)   (adjective)

the _____ chef in the country by _____ . It's amazing, but every year he
(adjective)   (name of magazine)

gets _____ and _____ .
(adjective)   (adjective)

Level 5 Unit 7 Adjectives (Use with pupil book pages 228–229.)
Skill: Students will use the correct forms of good and bad.

Name _____

5 LANGUAGE AND USAGE WORKBOOK PLUS ▲ 93

Proper Adjectives

Proper Nouns	Proper Adjectives
Africa	**African** fabrics
Greece	**Greek** olives
Central America	**Central American** food

A. Rewrite each sentence, using a proper adjective that is made from the proper noun in parentheses.

1. Bernardo saw __?__ linens at the world trade fair. (Ireland)
Bernardo saw Irish linens at the world trade fair.

2. __?__ cameras were also on display. (Japan)
Japanese cameras were also on display.

3. There was an exhibit of __?__ sculpture. (North Africa)
There was an exhibit of North African sculpture.

4. The __?__ sweaters looked warm. (Scotland)
The Scottish sweaters looked warm.

5. The __?__ jade came in different shades of green. (China)
The Chinese jade came in different shades of green.

6. Bernardo gazed at the __?__ baskets. (West Indies)
Bernardo gazed at the West Indian baskets.

7. He admired the __?__ carpets. (Belgium)
He admired the Belgian carpets.

8. He sampled some __?__ foods. (France)
He sampled some French foods.

9. The __?__ machinery exhibit impressed him. (Germany)
The German machinery exhibit impressed him.

10. The __?__ hosts had put on a good show. (North America)
The North American hosts had put on a good show.

(continued)

Level 5 Unit 7 Adjectives *(Use with pupil book pages 230–231.)*
Skill: Students will form proper adjectives from proper nouns.

Name _____

5 LANGUAGE AND USAGE WORKBOOK PLUS ▲ 94

Proper Adjectives *(continued from page 93)*

B. Writing Application: A List

You are a customs officer. Your job is to check the items that people bring into the United States from other countries. Make a list of ten items that you have checked. Use a different proper adjective to describe each item in your list. **Students to respond on separate paper. Answers will vary.**

Enrichment

Use the map to complete the sentences below. Write a proper adjective in each blank. You may use your dictionary.

1. Athens is the **Greek** capital.
2. Vienna is the **Austrian** capital.
3. Prague is the **Czech or Czechoslovakian** capital.
4. Warsaw is the **Polish** capital.
5. Lisbon is the **Portuguese** capital.
6. Bonn is the **West German** capital.
7. Budapest is the **Hungarian** capital.
8. Copenhagen is the **Danish** capital.
9. Bucharest is the **Rumanian or Romanian** capital.

Level 5 Unit 7 Adjectives *(Use with pupil book pages 230–231.)*
Skill: Students will form and use proper adjectives.

Page 95

COMPOSITION SKILL: DESCRIPTION

Using Sense Words

Sight: blue, straight, tiny, brick
Sound: silent, crashing, purring, roaring
Taste: sweet, sour, tangy, bitter
Smell: spicy, leathery, piny, soapy
Touch: slippery, mushy, sharp, cool

Use your five senses to describe the items below. Write as many sense words as you can to describe each item.
Answers will vary.

1. a skyscraper _____

2. the wind against your face _____

3. sand in your shoe _____

4. a telephone _____

5. an ambulance siren coming toward you _____

6. rain clouds _____

7. a frog _____

8. the first day of spring _____

9. the ocean _____

10. a baby _____

Level 5 Unit 8   Description   *(Use with pupil book pages 262–263.)*
Skill: Students will use sense words to describe how things look, sound, taste, smell, and feel.

Page 96

COMPOSITION SKILL: DESCRIPTION

Using Exact Words

Without Exact Words: My bike is pretty. It has some stuff.
With Exact Words: My new bike is bright green. It has a rack and a tool kit.

Rewrite the following paragraphs. Replace the underlined words with vivid and exact words.

A.   Gilbert was sad. In the ten years since he was born, this was the worst birthday he had ever had. No one remembered. He even had to stay after school for some reason. He went home and opened the door. He heard a sound: "Surprise!" People were in the dining room. Lots of things were on the table. Gilbert was happy. "You really fooled me!" he said.
Answers will vary.

_____
_____
_____
_____
_____
_____
_____

B.   The chipmunk took a nut and put it in its mouth. Its mouth was so full that its cheeks stuck out. We laughed hard. The chipmunk looked at us. The chipmunk moved its tail and went away.
Answers will vary.

_____
_____
_____
_____
_____
_____

Level 5 Unit 8   Description   *(Use with pupil book pages 263–264.)*
Skill: Students will rewrite paragraphs, using exact and vivid words.

Name _____

COMPOSITION SKILL: DESCRIPTION

Choosing Details

When you write a description, decide what impression you want to give your reader. Choose details to support your purpose.

Read the sentences below. Decide whether you want them to tell a happy story or a scary story. Then rewrite each sentence, adding at least two details that create an impression of happiness or fear.

Answers will vary.

1. Alonzo and I went for a walk one day.

_____

2. We went to the woods.

_____

3. We walked along a path.

_____

4. After a while, we came to a cave.

_____

5. There was a sign near it.

_____

6. The opening was large.

_____

7. Alonzo looked inside the cave.

_____

8. I called out.

_____

9. We went inside.

_____

10. "What a cave!" Alonzo said.

_____

Level 5 Unit 8 Description　*(Use with pupil book page 265.)*
Skill: Students will rewrite sentences, adding descriptive details that create a specific impression.

Name _____

COMPOSITION SKILL: DESCRIPTION

Organizing Your Description

Spatial order is one way to organize details in a description. Organize details from right to left, left to right, top to bottom, near to far, or far to near. Some spatial order words are *above, below, across, beside, opposite, inside, outside, next to, left, and right.*

You can also organize details in order of importance from the most to the least important or from the least to the most important. Some words that show the order of importance are *first, next, then, another, and finally.*

A. Write a list of five or six details describing your classroom. Organize your details from front to back. Use some words that tell the spatial order.

Answers will vary.

_____

_____

_____

_____

_____

B. Write a list of five or six details describing your classroom. This time organize your details from least to most important.

Answers will vary.

_____

_____

_____

_____

_____

Level 5 Unit 8 Description　*(Use with pupil book pages 266–267.)*
Skill: Students will list details for descriptions, using given spatial orders and words that signal those orders.

Step 4: Proofread

proofread writing mistakes
always ~~proofread~~ your ~~writing~~ for ~~mistake~~.

Proofreading Marks
⊄ Indent.
∧ Add something.
ℐ Take out something.
≡ Capitalize.
/ Make a small letter.

Proofread the following paragraph. Find four spelling errors, two capitalization errors, two punctuation errors, one run-on sentence, and one mistake in paragraph format. Find three errors in making comparisons with adjectives. Use proofreading marks to correct the errors. Use a dictionary to check your spelling.

⊄ Behind our home is a big apple tree. My Mother says that it was already there before I was born. In the Winter the branches tap loudly against the house. The wind blows loudly through the branches of the tree. I don't know whether the wind or the tree makes the louder noise. The branches are covered with white blossoms in the spring. When the apples get ripe, I climb on the branches there I have the most beautiful view of the neighborhood. Then I shake the branches. Some apples fall out of the tree, and I pick them up. I divide them into three groups. The perfect ones are for eating raw, and the ones with brown spots are for cooking applesauce. The ones with worm holes are the worst of all. They are thrown away.

Level 5 Unit 8 Description (Use with pupil book pages 273–274.)
Skill: Students will proofread a descriptive paragraph, correcting mistakes in spelling, punctuation, capitalization, paragraph format, and forms of comparison.

Step 3: Revise

Have I   yes

crossed out any details that do not support the purpose of the description? □

added sense words to describe how things look, smell, taste, sound, and feel? □

added exact words to help create a clear picture? □

changed the order of some sentences so that all the details are arranged in the same spatial order? □

Revise the following description. Use the check list above to help you. Check off each box when you have finished your revision.
• Use a thesaurus to help you find exact words.
• Use the space above each line and on the sides of the paragraph for your changes.
Sample answers:

This morning I took a walk in the first snow of the winter.
furry   footprints   freshly fallen, clean white
My boots made the first marks in the snow. The snow made noise.
                                           crunched and crumbled
under my feet. I looked around. The air was cool and crisp against
                              the white cloud of
my face. It seemed almost like spring. I could see my breath as I
breathed. At the next corner, snow-covered branches stretched in fantastic shapes
over the street. Just in front of me was a funny-looking heap of
blanketed with snow   and looked heavy with snow
snow. It was a car. The sky in the distance was gray. The sun was
                                        drifted lazily down
covered by a haze. As I looked up, a few snowflakes fell
                                        cold and light.
from the sky. I caught some on my tongue. They tasted fine. The
of winter   covered the world around me in a frosty white coverlet.
first snow had changed the way things looked.

Level 5 Unit 8 Description (Use with pupil book pages 271–272.)
Skill: Students will revise a description, crossing out details that do not fit the overall impression, adding sense words and exact words, and rearranging sentences to fit one spatial order.

Name _____

MECHANICS   WORKBOOK PLUS 102

1 Capitalizing and Punctuating Sentences (continued from page 101)

B. Writing Application: A Description
You see a very strange building. What is unusual about it? Write six sentences, describing the building. Include a declarative sentence, an interrogative sentence, an imperative sentence, and an exclamatory sentence in your description.
Students to respond on separate paper. Answers will vary.

Enrichment

The guide in the cartoons below is giving a tour of the Washington Monument. Write four captions, telling what is happening in these cartoons. Include a declarative sentence, an interrogative sentence, an imperative sentence, and an exclamatory sentence in your captions.

Answers will vary.

1.

2.
898 STEPS

3.

4.

Now draw your own cartoon about a tour of a building you know. Write a caption beneath your cartoon.

Level 5   Unit 9   Capitalization and Punctuation   (Use with pupil book pages 282–283.)
Skill: Students will write the four types of sentences correctly.

Name _____

MECHANICS   WORKBOOK PLUS 101

1 Capitalizing and Punctuating Sentences

> Declarative Sentence: A pentagon is a five-sided figure.
> Imperative Sentence: Please come to Washington.
> Interrogative Sentence: Is there a pentagon there?
> Exclamatory Sentence: I can't wait to see it!

A. Write each sentence correctly. Separate any run-on sentences.
Sample answers:
1. guess the size of the world's largest pentagon
   Guess the size of the world's largest pentagon.

2. how big is it
   How big is it?

3. this five-sided figure measures about one mile around
   This five-sided figure measures about one mile around.

4. take a closer look at the Pentagon Building how huge it is
   Take a closer look at the Pentagon Building. How huge it is!

5. it contains the United States Department of Defense
   It contains the United States Department of Defense.

6. what a huge department that is
   What a huge department that is!

7. do you know that about 25,000 people work in the Pentagon
   Do you know that about 25,000 people work in the Pentagon?

8. that's a lot of people to feed does it have a large food service
   That's a lot of people to feed! Does it have a large food service?

9. it has a bank and a post office it even has its own TV system
   It has a bank and a post office. It even has its own TV system.

10. go on a tour of the Pentagon tell me what you think of it
    Go on a tour of the Pentagon. Tell me what you think of it.

(continued)

Level 5   Unit 9   Capitalization and Punctuation   (Use with pupil book pages 282–283.)
Skill: Students will capitalize and will punctuate the four types of sentences.

2 | Proper Nouns and Proper Adjectives

| Proper Nouns: | Mexico | Taro Suzuki | Friday | Fourth of July |
| Proper Adjectives: | Mexican | Swiss | Greek | North American |

A. Find the proper noun or proper adjective in each sentence. Write it correctly.

1. My friend linda mendez has a coin collection. **Linda Mendez**

2. Some coins are from north african countries. **North African**

3. One egyptian coin is the size of a quarter. **Egyptian**

4. A coin from the republic of china has a hole. **Republic of China**

5. Recently she bought some ancient greek coins. **Greek**

6. One has a picture of alexander the great. **Alexander the Great**

7. Last monday she visited a coin exhibit. **Monday**

8. She spent columbus day at a museum. **Columbus Day**

9. It was the metropolitan museum of art. **Metropolitan Museum of Art**

10. The museum featured coins during october. **October**

11. There were displays of old roman coins. **Roman**

12. Some had been found in the red sea. **Red Sea**

13. A few came from ancient spanish ships. **Spanish**

14. The face of julius caesar decorated some. **Julius Caesar**

15. Some showed portraits of caesar augustus. **Caesar Augustus**

16. Her trip to new york city was worth the effort. **New York City**

17. Perhaps someday she will visit london. **London**

18. The british museum has a good collection. **British Museum**

19. The victoria and albert museum also has one. **Victoria and Albert Museum**

20. Some coin clubs tour the british isles. **British Isles**

(continued)

---

2 | Proper Nouns and Proper Adjectives (continued from page 103)

B. **Writing Application: A Diary**

Pretend that you are on a trip to a foreign country. Today you exchanged your money, toured a large city, and met a famous person. Write a diary entry, describing your day. Use at least three proper nouns and three proper adjectives. **Students to respond on separate paper. Answers will vary.**

★ Enrichment

You have been hired to design the money for a new country. Tell about the money by completing the sentences. Use a proper noun or a proper adjective in each answer.

1. The name of the country is **Answers will vary.** ____.

2. The money looks a little like ____ money.

3. The building you work in is called the ____.

4. The person on one bill is named ____.

5. That person is an important ____ citizen.

6. The person on another bill is named ____.

Use the forms below to draw two of the bills that you designed. Include the information given in the sentences that you just completed.

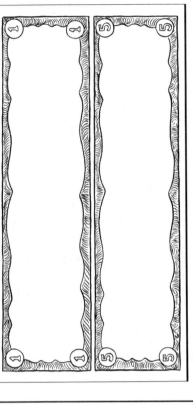

T51

Name _____

MECHANICS

3 ‖ Commas in a Series

My sister, my brother, and I watched the new family move in. We introduced ourselves, welcomed them, and invited them for dinner.

A. Rewrite each sentence that contains a series. Add commas where they are needed. For each sentence that does not include a series, write none.

1. Will Les Martha and Julie be going to our school?
   Will Les, Martha, and Julie be going to our school?

2. Les will be in the same class as Alfredo and I.
   none

3. His sisters are in the first third and fourth grades.
   His sisters are in the first, third, and fourth grades.

4. Let's invite them to play ball have a picnic swim or sunbathe.
   Let's invite them to play ball, have a picnic, swim, or sunbathe.

5. We could meet them at the park in the school yard or at my house.
   We could meet them at the park, in the school yard, or at my house.

6. Let's wait until Thursday Friday or the weekend.
   Let's wait until Thursday, Friday, or the weekend.

7. They just moved in and have a lot to do.
   none

8. Right now they must unpack clean and move furniture.
   Right now they must unpack, clean, and move furniture.

B. Add commas to these sentences. Make the two sentences in each pair have different meanings. Sample answers:

9. They ate cheese sandwiches tuna salad and eggs.
   Les James, Martha, May, and Julie had a picnic in the park.
   Les James, Martha May, and Julie had a picnic in the park.

10. They ate cheese sandwiches tuna salad and eggs.
    They ate cheese sandwiches, tuna, salad, and eggs.
    They ate cheese sandwiches, tuna salad, and eggs.

(continued)

Name _____

MECHANICS

3 ‖ Commas in a Series *(continued from page 105)*

C. Writing Application: A Newsletter

Pretend that you write a neighborhood newsletter. A new family has moved into your neighborhood. Write at least five sentences about who is in the family and what the neighbors are doing to welcome them. Use a series in each of your sentences.
Students to respond on separate paper. Answers will vary.

★ **Enrichment** ★

Read the words written on the blackboard. Find words and phrases that can be grouped together. Write each group on the lines below.

history	pens	in the cafeteria	mathematics
interesting	in the library	rewarding	challenging
rulers	tuna sandwich	pencils	banana
applesauce	play chess	edit the	science
social studies	erasers	newspaper	
design a mural	milk	on the field	

Sample answers:

1. history
   social studies
   mathematics
   science

2. design a mural
   play chess
   edit the newspaper

3. rulers
   pens
   erasers
   pencils

4. interesting
   rewarding
   challenging

5. tuna sandwich
   applesauce
   milk
   banana

6. in the library
   in the cafeteria
   on the field

Now, on another piece of paper, write six sentences, telling new students about your school. Use each of the above groups of words in a series. Remember to use commas correctly.

MECHANICS

4 | More Uses for Commas *(continued from page 107)*

B. Writing Application: A Note

You know someone who is in the hospital. Write a note to wish that person a speedy recovery. Use the person's name at least three times in your note. Use the introductory words *oh, yes, well,* and *no* at least once. Remember to use commas correctly.

Students to respond on separate paper. Answers will vary.

Enrichment

Study the cartoons below. Think of a story that will fit the pictures. Write what each character is saying. Use an introductory word or a noun in direct address in each speech balloon. Remember to use commas correctly.
Answers will vary.

Now draw your own cartoon on another piece of paper. Use an introductory word or a noun in direct address in each speech balloon.

Level 5 Unit 9 Capitalization and Punctuation *(Use with pupil book pages 288–289.)*
Skill: Students will use introductory words and nouns in direct address in sentences.

MECHANICS

4 | More Uses for Commas

Introductory Words:	Oh, I heard about your class. Yes, it's great!
Nouns in Direct Address:	Elsa, come to my class with me.
	You will enjoy it, Elsa.
	You will see, Elsa, that it is useful.

A. Rewrite each sentence, adding commas where they are needed.

1. Yolanda I hear that you're taking a course in first aid.
   Yolanda, I hear that you're taking a course in first aid.

2. Yes Willy I'm taking a course with Ms. Liang.
   Yes, Willy, I'm taking a course with Ms. Liang.

3. Can you tell me more about the course Yolanda?
   Can you tell me more about the course, Yolanda?

4. Well Willy I've only had one class.
   Well, Willy, I've only had one class.

5. I wonder Yolanda if it's too late for me to sign up.
   I wonder, Yolanda, if it's too late for me to sign up.

6. No I don't believe it is.
   No, I don't believe it is.

7. Why don't you come with me Willy?
   Why don't you come with me, Willy?

8. Oh Ms. Liang let me introduce you to Willy.
   Oh, Ms. Liang, let me introduce you to Willy.

9. Well you're just in time Willy to help with a demonstration.
   Well, you're just in time, Willy, to help with a demonstration.

10. Yolanda help me put Willy's arm in this sling.
    Yolanda, help me put Willy's arm in this sling.

(continued)

Level 5 Unit 9 Capitalization and Punctuation *(Use with pupil book pages 288–289.)*
Skill: Students will use commas to set off introductory words and nouns in direct address.

Name _____

5 MECHANICS
| Interjections |

Hey! Try to find some good seats.
Oh, the balloon rally is starting!

A. Complete each line of this skit, using the interjection in parentheses. Use the correct punctuation after each interjection.

1. Safa: _____**Great!**_____ The colors are fantastic! **(Great)**

2. Lois: _____**Wow!**_____ That green one is the highest. **(Wow)**

3. Willy: _____**Ah,**_____ what a beautiful sight! **(Ah)**

4. Lois: _____**Hey!**_____ Hot-air ballooning might be fun. **(Hey)**

5. Safa: _**Good grief!**_ It's too early in the morning. **(Good grief)**

6. Willy: _____**Well,**_____ it's less windy in the morning. **(Well)**

7. Safa: _____**Oh,**_____ a strong wind could be dangerous! **(Oh)**

8. Lois: _____**Ha!**_____ Look at the tiny baskets! **(Ha)**

9. Willy: _**Goodness!**_ There are two people in each basket. **(Goodness)**

10. Safa: _____**Well,**_____ a larger balloon carries even more weight! **(Well)**

11. Lois: _____**Oops!**_____ One balloon is descending early! **(Oops)**

12. Willy: _____**Whew!**_____ It landed safely. **(Whew)**

13. Safa: _____**Hey,**_____ guess who the first balloonists were! **(Hey)**

14. Lois: _____**Oh, no!**_____ Is this a joke? **(Oh, no)**

15. Safa: _____**Ha,**_____ a duck, a sheep, and a rooster were the first! **(Ha)**

B. Writing Application: A Skit

You and a friend are discussing a rubber raft trip that you have recently taken. Write a skit, using interjections to show feeling or emotion. Remember to use either an exclamation point or a comma after each interjection.

(continued)

Level 5   Unit 9   Capitalization and Punctuation   *(Use with pupil book pages 290–291.)*
Skill: Students will use commas and exclamation points to punctuate interjections.

Name _____

5 MECHANICS
| Interjections | *(continued from page 109)*

★ **Enrichment** ★

The characters in the cartoon below are enjoying their first balloon vacation. Tell what each is saying about the view below them. Write a sentence in each speech balloon. Begin each one with an interjection. Use the correct punctuation after each interjection.
Answers will vary.

Level 5   Unit 9   Capitalization and Punctuation   *(Use with pupil book pages 290–291.)*
Skill: Students will use interjections in sentences.

T55

Name _____

MECHANICS

6 | Quotations

> The firefighter exclaimed, "Fire safety is important!"
> "You should know what to do in case of fire," she added.
> "There are rules," she explained, "that you should follow."
> "You must know some," she said. "Can you remember them?"

A. Rewrite each sentence, using punctuation marks and capital letters correctly.

1. the firefighter announced there are rules for fire safety

   The firefighter announced, "There are rules for fire safety."

2. let's see if you know what they are she added

   "Let's see if you know what they are," she added.

3. take care of flammable liquids said Tim keep them far from heat

   "Take care of flammable liquids," said Tim. "Keep them far from heat."

4. should electrical wiring Mark asked be checked carefully

   "Should electrical wiring," Mark asked, "be checked carefully?"

5. never overload an electrical outlet Judy exclaimed

   "Never overload an electrical outlet!" Judy exclaimed.

6. Tim reminded don't stack newspapers, rags, or paints in basements.

   Tim reminded, "Don't stack newspapers, rags, or paints in basements."

7. plan escape routes suggested Judy in case of fire

   "Plan escape routes," suggested Judy, "in case of fire."

8. have you ever held a fire drill in your home asked the firefighter

   "Have you ever held a fire drill in your home?" asked the firefighter.

9. Mark exclaimed we certainly have

   Mark exclaimed, "We certainly have!"

10. Tim sighed we should all check our homes more carefully

    Tim sighed, "We should all check our homes more carefully."

(continued)

Level 5   Unit 9   Capitalization and Punctuation   (Use with pupil book pages 292–293.)
Skill: Students will capitalize and will punctuate direct quotations.

Name _____

MECHANICS

6 | Quotations   (continued from page 111)

B. Writing Application: A Dialogue

You and a friend are having a conversation about fire safety. Your friend is asking you about safety precautions you take in your home, and you are answering. Write the dialogue, using direct quotations. Remember to use capital letters and punctuation marks correctly.
Students to respond on separate paper. Answers will vary.

⭐ **Enrichment** ⭐

The students below drew posters to illustrate their reports on school fire drills. Use the posters to help you decide what each student is saying about fire safety. Then write a direct quotation for each picture.   **Sample answers:**

1.

   Mike said, "Know where the fire alarm is in your building."

2.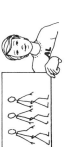

   "Form a line," suggested Al.

3.

   "Use the stairs," Lucia explained, "not the elevator."

4.

   "Don't talk," said Ellen. "You need to listen to instructions."

5.

   "Close the windows," reminded Stella, "before leaving the room."

6.

   "Always walk," added Lee. "Never run."

Level 5   Unit 9   Capitalization and Punctuation   (Use with pupil book pages 292–293.)
Skill: Students will write direct quotations correctly.

Page 113

Name _____

MECHANICS

7 | Abbreviations

Titles:	Mister	Mr.	Junior	Jr.
	a married woman	Mrs.	Senior	Sr.
	any woman	Ms.	Doctor	Dr.
Businesses:	Corporation	Corp.	Limited	Ltd.
Days:	Tuesday	Tues.	Sunday	Sun.
Months:	February	Feb.	August	Aug.
Addresses:	Apartment	Apt.	Route	Rte.
States:	California	CA	Illinois	IL
Initials:	Susan Gloria	S. G.	Ling Chow	L. C.

A. Write these groups of words, using the correct abbreviations and initials.

1. Audio Service Corporation ___**Audio Service Corp.**___

2. Wednesday, September 29, 1875 ___**Wed., Sept. 29, 1875**___

3. Alva John Holmes, Senior ___**A. J. Holmes, Sr.**___

4. Rodriguez, Incorporated ___**Rodriguez, Inc.**___

5. Friday, August 13, 1990 ___**Fri., Aug. 13, 1990**___

B. Write these addresses. Use the correct abbreviations and initials for the underlined words.

6. Doctor Jane Wilbur ___**Dr. J. Wilbur**___

    Route 30 ___**Rte. 30**___

    Richmond, Virginia 23219 ___**Richmond, VA 23219**___

7. Four Star Company, Limited ___**Four Star Co., Ltd.**___

    Post Office Box 5555 ___**P.O. Box 5555**___

    Dallas, Texas 75234 ___**Dallas, TX 75234**___

8. Mister Alonso Richard Amanda ___**Mr. A. R. Amanda**___

    2001 Brentwood Avenue ___**2001 Brentwood Ave.**___

    Springfield, Illinois 62704 ___**Springfield, IL 62704**___

(continued)

Level 5 Unit 9 Capitalization and Punctuation *(Use with pupil book pages 294–295.)*
Skill: Students will write abbreviations correctly.

Page 114

Name _____

MECHANICS

7 | Abbreviations *(continued from page 113)*

C. Writing Application: An Invitation

Write an invitation to invite your aunt to a school play. Include the date, the time of the play, and the address of your school. Use at least five abbreviations. **Students to respond on separate paper. Answers will vary.**

★ **Enrichment** ★

Use the code in the chart below to solve the puzzles. First, find the abbreviation for each state in the numbered list. Then write the letter the abbreviation stands for above the number of the state. The first one has been done for you.

CA	NY	TX	OR	IN	AL	DE	WA	VT	TN	ND	AK	IL
A	B	C	D	E	F	G	H	I	J	K	L	M
OH	NM	GA	NE	FL	MI	CT	ME	CO	MO	SC	VA	KY
N	O	P	Q	R	S	T	U	V	W	X	Y	Z

1. California
2. New York
3. New York
4. Florida
5. Indiana
6. Colorado
7. Vermont
8. California
9. Connecticut
10. Vermont
11. New Mexico
12. Ohio
13. Michigan
14. Texas
15. California
16. Ohio
17. New York
18. Indiana
19. Alabama
20. Maine
21. Ohio

A B B R E V I A T I O N S
1 2 3 4 5 6 7 8 9 10 11 12 13

C A N B E F U N !
14 15 16 17 8 18 19 20 21

Now solve this puzzle. Use the same code.

1. Virginia
2. New Mexico
3. Maine
4. California
5. Florida
6. Indiana
7. California
8. Texas
9. New Mexico
10. Oregon
11. Indiana
12. California
13. Florida
14. Indiana
15. California

Y O U   A R E
1 2 3   4 5 6

C O D E   B R E A K E R !
8 9 10 11   12 13 14 15 16 17 18

A
7

Level 5 Unit 9 Capitalization and Punctuation *(Use with pupil book pages 294–295.)*
Skill: Students will use abbreviations correctly.

8 Titles

I read the book The Prince and the Pauper.
I read The Daily Star every morning.
The chorus sang "Home on the Range."
We read the poem "The Song of the Desert."

A. Write each sentence correctly.

1. Today's parktown crier, our newspaper, contained lots of information.
   Today's Parktown Crier, our newspaper, contained lots of information.

2. Joanna read a review of the book called the black stallion.
   Joanna read a review of the book called The Black Stallion.

3. She is now reading the chapter called homeward bound.
   She is now reading the chapter called "Homeward Bound."

4. Tod saw a review of the movie chariots of fire.
   Tod saw a review of the movie Chariots of Fire.

5. Now he's writing his own story, run for the gold.
   Now he's writing his own story, "Run for the Gold."

6. Zelda read a report in the magazine called time.
   Zelda read a report in the magazine called Time.

7. She wanted to read an article called our changing language.
   She wanted to read an article called "Our Changing Language."

8. It contained the poem space rhymes.
   It contained the poem "Space Rhymes."

9. Marco read about an old song called mr. tambourine man.
   Marco read about an old song called "Mr. Tambourine Man."

10. Then Marco wrote a song of his own called a banjo player.
    Then Marco wrote a song of his own called "A Banjo Player."

(continued)

---

8 Titles   *(continued from page 115)*

B. Writing Application: A Letter

Your pen pal has asked you to recommend some books and movies. Write a letter to your pen pal, recommending your favorite book, short story, magazine, movie, poem, and song. Be sure to write the titles correctly. **Students to respond on separate paper. Answers will vary.**

★ Enrichment ★

You are the editor of your school newspaper. Below is a layout for the front page of the paper. Each block contains a brief description of a story. Write a name for the newspaper in the top space. Then think of a title for each story. Write the title above the description of the story.

VOL. XXIX   *   *   *   *   *   *   MARCH 21, 1990

Answers will vary.

a poem about homework	a short story about a mountain-climbing expedition	an article about the crowded conditions in the cafeteria
a review of a new magazine for teen-agers	a movie review	a book review

Now, on another piece of paper, write a report to your teacher, telling about the subject of each article. Write six sentences. Include the title of a poem, a magazine, a short story, a movie, or a book in each sentence.

T57

Name _____

Writing Business Letters

A **business letter** is usually written for a purpose—to request information, order a product, apply for a job. Like a friendly letter, it has a heading, greeting, body, closing, and signature. It also has an *inside address*. When you write a business letter, use a colon (:) after the greeting. Close with *Sincerely* or *Yours truly*. Sign your full name.

A. Complete the business letter below. Address the letter to the Order Department. Request one copy of Birds of the Northeast that was advertised in the magazine Wildlife. Make up information to fill in any of the missing parts. Use the inside address given below.

Order Department
Wildlife, Inc.
P.O. Box 349
Los Angeles, CA 90004
Answers will vary.

_____
_____
_____
_____
_____
_____
_____
_____
_____
_____
_____
_____

(continued)

Name _____

Writing Business Letters (continued from page 117)

B. Write a business letter on the blanks below to Houghton Mifflin Company. Request a new catalogue of the books that the company publishes. Use your own address and today's date in the heading. Use the inside address below.

Houghton Mifflin Company
2 Park Street
Boston, MA 02108
Answers will vary.

_____
_____
_____
_____
_____
_____
_____
_____
_____
_____
_____
_____
_____
_____
_____
_____
_____

Page 119

COMPOSITION SKILL: PERSUASIVE LETTER

Stating and Supporting an Opinion

> State your opinion clearly and support it with strong reasons. To persuade others to accept your opinion, give reasons that will appeal to them.

Read the two opinion statements below. Then write four strong supporting reasons for each opinion. Use reasons that would appeal to an audience of your own age.
Answers will vary.

A. It is better to live in the country than in the city.

Reason 1: _____

Reason 2: _____

Reason 3: _____

Reason 4: _____

B. It is better to live in the city than in the country.

Reason 1: _____

Reason 2: _____

Reason 3: _____

Reason 4: _____

Page 120

COMPOSITION SKILL: PERSUASIVE LETTER

Ordering Your Reasons

> Put reasons for an opinion in an order that will convince your audience, from *most* important to *least* important or from *least* important to *most* important.

Choose two of the topics listed below. Write a sentence for each one, stating an opinion about the topic. Then think of four reasons that can help you persuade your classmates to accept your opinion. Write your reasons on the blanks below in the order that you think will be most convincing to your audience.
Answers will vary.

| gym for everyone every day | class party on the last day of school |
| lessons for emergency first aid | student art display in the front hall |

A. **Topic Sentence:** _____

   Reasons: _____

   _____

   _____

   _____

B. **Topic Sentence:** _____

   Reasons: _____

   _____

   _____

   _____

Name _____

Step 4: Proofread

Proofreading Marks
⌐P Indent.
∧ Add something.
✗ Take out something.
≡ Capitalize.
/ Make a small letter.

Please send the ⌃booklet on a farmer's life, work̶, and rewards⊙

Proofread this business letter. Find three spelling errors, four capitalization errors, five punctuation errors, and one run-on sentence. Use proofreading marks to correct the errors. Use a dictionary to check your spelling.

4111 Spring garden Street
                    ≡
Phillipsburg⌃NJ 08865

September 25⌃1990

To-A-Tee Shirt company
                    ≡
128 Ridge avenue
          ≡
Norwalk, Ct 06854
        ≡

Dear Sir or Madam⌃

             council   launching
Our student counsel̶ is launching⌃a campaign to get more people to

vote. We want to sell T-shirts saying VOTING IS FREE. We'll sell
                                                            neighbors
them to our parents, relatives⌃and neibors̶⌃will you make these shirts for
                                              ≡
us? If so, how much will they cost⌃?

Name _____

Step 3: Revise

Have I   yes

rewritten the topic sentence so that it clearly states the
opinion?   ☐

rewritten weak reasons to make them stronger and crossed
out reasons that do not support the opinion?   ☐

added reasons that will be convincing to the audience?   ☐

arranged the reasons in order from most important to least
important?   ☐

Revise the following persuasive letter. Use the check list above to help you.
Check off each box when you have finished your revision.
• Use the space above each line, on the sides, and below the letter for your
changes.
Sample answers:

Dear City Council Members:

    Our city should have bike paths. They would make the
⌃Bike paths are a good idea. Don't you think that our
city a much safer place.
city should have them? More people would ride bicycles if they
had a safe place to ride them. Bike paths would be pretty too.
Flowers could be planted along the sides. There have been many
accidents between cars and bicycles in our city. People have
      Many people s   or work   they
been badly hurt. I ride my bike to school, and I have to ride on
busy streets because there is nowhere else to ride. I hope that
you will consider my reasons and vote to build bike paths in our
city. This would mean fewer cars on the roads.

Level 5   Unit 10   Persuasive Letter   (Use with pupil book pages 335–336.)
Skill: Students will revise a persuasive letter, rewriting the topic sentence, rewriting, removing, or adding
reasons, and rearranging reasons in most to least important order.

LANGUAGE AND USAGE

1 Subject Pronouns

Nouns	Subject Pronouns
Manuel and Judy heard a speech.	**They** heard a speech.
The speaker was Mrs. Ruiz.	The speaker was **she**.

A. Write the subject pronoun that could replace the underlined word or words.

1. Manuel, Judy, and I have been reading about dinosaurs. — **We**
2. Dinosaurs became extinct millions of years ago. — **They**
3. The best-informed student is Manuel. — **he**
4. Judy and Manuel read about the brontosaur. — **he**
5. The brontosaur was one of the largest dinosaurs. — **It**
6. How large was this dinosaur? — **it**
7. Judy and I made a chart. — **We**
8. The chart gave a description of several dinosaurs. — **It**
9. The allosaurus and the stegosaur were included. — **They**
10. Judy showed the chart to Mrs. Ruiz and Mr. Li. — **She**
11. The science teacher is Mrs. Ruiz. — **she**
12. Mr. Li is an expert on dinosaurs. — **He**
13. A recent speaker at the science fair was Mr. Li. — **he**
14. The science fair was visited by several paleontologists. — **It**
15. Paleontologists are scientists who study fossils. — **They**
16. Fossils are prints found in rocks. — **They**
17. Judy and I learned a great deal from these scientists. — **We**
18. The person who was most impressed by the fair was Judy. — **she**
19. Next week Judy will visit the Museum of Natural History. — **she**
20. The museum has a wonderful display of dinosaur skeletons. — **It**

(continued)

LANGUAGE AND USAGE

1 Subject Pronouns *(continued from page 123)*

B. Writing Application: A Paragraph

You and your friends suddenly find yourselves living in the time of the dinosaurs. Write a paragraph about what you see. Use at least five subject pronouns in your paragraph. Underline each subject pronoun. Answers will vary.

Students to respond on separate paper. Answers will vary.

Enrichment

Melissa Spencer and several other scientists have uncovered the skeleton of an enormous dinosaur. Melissa wants to telegraph her college to tell about her discovery. However, her message is too long. Rewrite the message, replacing nouns with subject pronouns. Make sure the message still makes sense.

WESTERN TELEGRAPH TELEGRAM

The other scientists and Melissa Spencer found the skeleton of a dinosaur STOP Melissa and the scientists think that the dinosaur weighed one hundred tons STOP The dinosaur was probably one hundred and twenty feet long STOP Several bones have already been uncovered STOP These bones still must be cleaned and identified STOP Melissa will be forwarding photographs of this discovery immediately STOP

Melissa Spencer

Sample answer:

The other scientists and I found the skeleton of a dinosaur STOP We think that it weighed one hundred tons STOP It was probably one hundred and twenty feet long STOP Several bones have been uncovered STOP They still must be cleaned and identified STOP I will be forwarding photographs of this discovery immediately STOP

Now figure out the cost of the original telegram. There is a charge of $8.75 for the first ten words and $.45 for each additional word. Do not count the word STOP or Melissa's signature. Then figure out the cost of the rewritten telegram. How much money could Melissa have saved by using pronouns?

Sample answers:

Original Telegram: **$29.90**   Rewritten Telegram: **$26.75**

Savings: **$3.15**

Workbook Page 125

Name _____

2 Object Pronouns

Nouns	Object Pronouns
The Kents welcomed Fern.	The Kents welcomed **her.**
Fern went with the Kents.	Fern went with **them.**
Subject Pronoun	**Object Pronoun**
It was an interesting tour.	Fern liked **it.**

A. Rewrite these sentences, using the correct pronouns.

1. Mr. and Mrs. Kent gave Fern and (I, me) a tour of the bee farm.
Mr. and Mrs. Kent gave Fern and me a tour of the bee farm.

2. This was the first visit for (she, her) and (I, me).
This was the first visit for her and me.

3. Mr. Kent told (we, us) that beekeepers are called apiculturists.
Mr. Kent told us that beekeepers are called apiculturists.

4. (I, Me) asked (he, him) why beekeepers wear such strange clothing.
I asked him why beekeepers wear such strange clothing.

5. The clothes protect (they, them) from bee stings.
The clothes protect them from bee stings.

6. The Kents put beekeepers' veils on (we, us).
The Kents put beekeepers' veils on us.

7. (We, Us) followed (he, him) and (she, her) into the field.
We followed him and her into the field.

8. Mrs. Kent cautioned Fern and (I, me) to move slowly.
Mrs. Kent cautioned Fern and me to move slowly.

9. (She, Her) explained to (we, us) that bees are social insects.
She explained to us that bees are social insects.

10. (We, Us) watched (they, them) communicate by dancing.
We watched them communicate by dancing.

(continued)

Workbook Page 126

Name _____

2 Object Pronouns (continued from page 125)

B. Writing Application: An Advertisement

You work in the advertising department of a book publishing company. Your assignment is to write an advertisement for a new book about bees. Tell why the book would be interesting to beekeepers, students, and scientists. Use subject and object pronouns in your advertisement. Underline the subject pronouns once and the object pronouns twice.
Students to respond on separate paper. Answers will vary.

Enrichment

Mr. Kent has decided to post signs around the beehives, warning visitors about possible dangers. Help Mr. Kent by writing four warning sentences. Include at least one object pronoun in each warning.

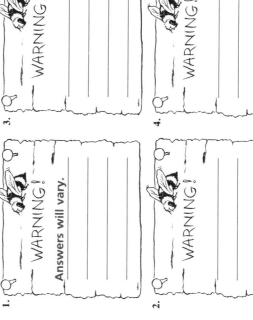

1. WARNING! **Answers will vary.**

2. WARNING!

3. WARNING!

4. WARNING!

LANGUAGE AND USAGE

3 | Using *I* and *me* (continued from page 127)

B. Writing Application: A Personal Narrative

Write about a trip you have taken with a friend. Write at least five sentences, telling where you went and what you saw. Use *I* or *me* in each sentence.
Students to respond on separate paper. Answers will vary.

★ Enrichment ★

Underline the correct pronoun in parentheses to complete each riddle. Then write the answer to each riddle.
Sample answers:

1. (I, Me) have holes on my sides. You put (I, me) in a camera. You need the camera and (I, me) to take photographs.
I am ___ **film** ___.

2. You can find my friends and (I, me) in museums. Sometimes (I, me) am black and white. Sometimes people take (I, me) with color film.
I am a ___ **photograph** ___.

3. Sometimes (I, me) am made of leather. (I, Me) have a strap. You can carry a camera in (I, me).
I am a ___ **camera bag** ___.

4. Sometimes (I, me) am made of metal. (I, Me) have three legs. You use (I, me) to steady a camera.
I am a ___ **tripod** ___.

5. (I, Me) am made of paper. You can display photographs in (I, me). (I, Me) usually have a hard cover.
I am a ___ **photograph album** ___.

6. (I, Me) am a place. There are no lights in (I, me). You can develop photographs in (I, me).
I am a ___ **darkroom** ___.

Now, on another piece of paper, write two riddles of your own. Use the pronoun *I* or *me* in each sentence.

Level 5 Unit 11 Pronouns (Use with pupil book pages 350–351.)
Skill: Students will use *I* and *me* correctly.

LANGUAGE AND USAGE

3 | Using *I* and *me*

| Ella and **I** enjoy photography. | I enjoy photography. |
| Dad shows his photos to Ella and **me**. | Dad shows his photos to **me**. |

A. Rewrite each sentence, using the correct word or words in parentheses.

1. Ella and (I, me) went to a photography show.
Ella and I went to a photography show.

2. It was an interesting experience for Ella and (I, me).
It was an interesting experience for Ella and me.

3. Dad decided not to go with Ella and (I, me).
Dad decided not to go with Ella and me.

4. He told (me and her, her and me) how to get to the show.
He told her and me how to get to the show.

5. Ella and (I, me) took the bus.
Ella and I took the bus.

6. The guide at the show spoke to Ella and (I, me).
The guide at the show spoke to Ella and me.

7. Then she showed Ella and (I, me) the pictures.
Then she showed Ella and me the pictures.

8. (She and I, I and she) liked a picture of a sad woman.
She and I liked a picture of a sad woman.

9. The guide told (I, me) that it was called *Migrant Mother*.
The guide told me that it was called Migrant Mother.

10. Ella and (I, me) learned that the photographer was Dorothea Lange.
Ella and I learned that the photographer was Dorothea Lange.

(continued)

Level 5 Unit 11 Pronouns (Use with pupil book pages 350–351.)
Skill: Students will use *I* and *me* correctly.

Name _____

4 | Possessive Pronouns

Before Nouns	Stand Alone
Her book is interesting.	The interesting book is **hers**.
My book is long.	**Mine** is long.

A. Rewrite each sentence, using the correct possessive pronoun in parentheses.

1. Today (our, ours) school is sponsoring a book fair.
   Today our school is sponsoring a book fair.

2. Has (your, yours) ever had such an event?
   Has yours ever had such an event?

3. (Our, ours) required a lot of preparation.
   Ours required a lot of preparation.

4. Actually (my, mine) teacher suggested the idea.
   Actually my teacher suggested the idea.

5. The idea of inviting famous authors was also (her, hers).
   The idea of inviting famous authors was also hers.

6. Peggy Parish and Steven Kellogg will talk about (their, theirs) works.
   Peggy Parish and Steven Kellogg will talk about their works.

7. Peggy Parish will read from (her, hers) novel *Key to the Treasure*.
   Peggy Parish will read from her novel Key to the Treasure.

8. *Pirate Island Adventure* is also (her, hers).
   Pirate Island Adventure is also hers.

9. After the fair, I will ask for (your, yours) comments.
   After the fair, I will ask for your comments.

10. Then I will give you (my, mine).
    Then I will give you mine.

(continued)

Name _____

4 | Possessive Pronouns   *(continued from page 129)*

B. Writing Application: Sentences

You and your friends are setting up a library for the younger children in your neighborhood. Write at least five sentences that tell what books you will have and who will donate the books. Use at least five different possessive pronouns. **Students to respond on separate paper. Answers will vary.**

⭐ Enrichment ⭐

Find out what type of book each student enjoys reading. Use the clues below the chart to help you find the answers. Place an X under each category that you eliminate. Then draw a star in the box that shows what type of book each student likes best.

	Legend	Biography	Mystery	Science
Lee	X	X	★	X
Bonnie	X	X	X	★
Maria	★	X	X	X
Seth	X	★	X	X

CLUES
- No person's name begins with the same letter as his or her favorite type of book.
- Bonnie and Seth don't enjoy works of fiction.
- Lee and Maria don't like books that are nonfiction.

Now write a sentence that tells about each person's favorite type of book. Use a possessive pronoun in each sentence. **Sample answers:**

1. Lee: **His favorite type of book is a mystery.**
2. Bonnie: **Hers are science books.**
3. Maria: **Her favorite types of books are legends.**
4. Seth: **His are biographies.**
5. Bonnie and Seth: **Their favorites are nonfiction.**
6. Lee and Maria: **Theirs are works of fiction.**

LANGUAGE AND USAGE

5 | Contractions with Pronouns

Pronoun + Verb	Contraction	Pronoun + Verb	Contraction
I am	I'm	we would	we'd
it is	it's	I have	I've
you are	you're	he has	he's
I will	I'll	you had	you'd

A. Write the contractions that can be made from the underlined words.

1. I have always liked big cats as much as Kim does.   **I've**

2. She is reading about lions and tigers now.   **She's**

3. She has purchased many posters of leopards and panthers.   **She's**

4. We are going to see an exhibit about big cats.   **We're**

5. I am impressed with their strength and grace.   **I'm**

6. I will take pictures of the exhibit.   **I'll**

7. You may come with us if you would like.   **you'd**

8. It is an interesting way to spend an afternoon.   **It's**

9. The speaker will discuss the cats that we have read about.   **we've**

10. He will tell about the spotted members of the cat family.   **He'll**

11. They are the most interesting to Kim.   **They're**

12. They have adapted to their changing environment.   **They've**

B. Write the pronoun and the verb that were combined to form the contraction in each sentence.

13. I'd go to Africa or Asia if I had the chance.   **I would**

14. My friend Paul told me that he's been to Africa.   **he has**

15. There you'll see lions in groups called prides.   **you will**

16. It's easy to find tigers in some parts of Asia.   **It is**

17. They'll be near water during the hot months.   **They will**

18. You'd have a wonderful time in Asia and Africa.   **You would**

(continued)

LANGUAGE AND USAGE

5 | Contractions with Pronouns   *(continued from page 131)*

C. Writing Application: A Diary

You have been on a trip to Africa. While you were there, you photographed many wild animals. Write a diary entry about your adventures. Include at least five contractions that are made from pronouns and verbs. **Students to respond on separate paper. Answers will vary.**

★ Enrichment

Below are pictures that you took of big cats during a trip to Africa and Asia. Write a caption, telling what is happening in each picture. Each caption should be a complete sentence. The sentences can be humorous or factual. Use a different contraction in each sentence.

Sample answers:

LIONS

1. He's resting with his cubs.

2. They're hunting a zebra.

LEOPARDS AND JAGUARS

3. They've had a hard day playing.

4. It's a perfect day for a swim.

TIGERS

5. She'll hide in the tall grass.

6. My, what big teeth you've grown!

Name _____

LANGUAGE AND USAGE

6 | Double Subjects

Incorrect:	These **plants they** lived long ago.
Correct:	These **plants** lived long ago.
	They lived long ago.

A. Rewrite each sentence, correcting the double subject.
Sample answers:
1. Poco and Marie they were collecting rocks for a science project.
   Poco and Marie were collecting rocks for a science project.

2. Marie she found a piece of shiny black rock.
   Marie found a piece of shiny black rock.

3. Poco he studied the piece carefully.
   Poco studied the piece carefully.

4. The rock it contained the print of a fern.
   The rock contained the print of a fern.

5. The print it is called a fossil.
   The print is called a fossil.

6. Fossils they tell about the past.
   Fossils tell about the past.

7. Sometimes animal bones or shells they turn to stone.
   Sometimes animal bones or shells turn to stone.

8. This process it takes millions of years.
   This process takes millions of years.

9. Poco he was impressed by Marie's discovery.
   Poco was impressed by Marie's discovery.

10. Later, Marie she showed the class the fossil.
    Later, Marie showed the class the fossil.

(continued)

Level 5 Unit 11 Pronouns *(Use with pupil book pages 356–357.)*
Skill: Students will correct double subjects.

Name _____

LANGUAGE AND USAGE

6 | Double Subjects *(continued from page 133)*

B. Writing Application: A Description

Imagine that you are a rock in the forest. You have been there thousands of years. Write a description of the people, the animals, or the plants that you have seen. Do not use any double subjects in your description.
Students to respond on separate paper. Answers will vary.

★ **Enrichment** ★

A paleontologist, a scientist who studies fossils, is a kind of detective. You, too, can be a detective. Use the words on each fossil to make a sentence. There is one extra word on each fossil. Cross out that word. Then rewrite the correct sentence on the line. Sample answers:

1.
   like somewhat mammoths
   elephants the ~~they~~ Asian
   and African looked

   Mammoths looked somewhat like the African and Asian elephants.

2.
   made years unusual an
   scientist ~~he~~ a ago
   discovery several

   Several years ago, a scientist made an unusual discovery.

3.
   found ~~it~~ frozen an the in
   ground mammoth was ancient

   An ancient mammoth was found in the frozen ground.

4.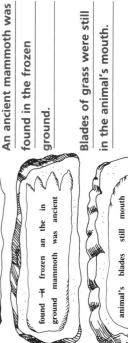
   animal's blades still mouth
   ~~they~~ of were grass the in

   Blades of grass were still in the animal's mouth.

Level 5 Unit 11 Pronouns *(Use with pupil book pages 356–357.)*
Skill: Students will correct double subjects.

LANGUAGE AND USAGE

7 | Using *we* and *us* with Nouns

> We students have a problem. Those with no money are **we** children.
> Dad gave **us** boys a lecture. He often talks to **us** children about money.

A. Write *we* or *us* to complete each sentence correctly.

1. Sports equipment is expensive for __us__ athletes.
2. __We__ artists always seem to need paint supplies.
3. The biggest spenders are __we__ students who are interested in fashion.
4. Obviously __we__ spenders never have any money.
5. __We__ children must earn some money.
6. Earning money does not come easily to __us__ young people.
7. Bankers won't lend money to __us__ children.
8. Those who have money will be __we__ workers.
9. Selling plants is a possibility for __us__ gardeners.
10. Neighbors will also give __us__ students some business.
11. They will hire __us__ gardeners to trim their lawns.
12. There are plenty of jobs for __us__ fence painters.
13. Often __we__ friends work together.
14. The children most often hired are __we__ people who do odd jobs.
15. __We__ delivery people can carry groceries and packages.
16. Drivers constantly hire __us__ car washers.
17. The ones always in demand are __we__ house cleaners.
18. There are many jobs for __us__ baby sitters too.
19. Our parents will be proud of __us__ workers.
20. Of course, those who will keep the most money are __we__ savers!

(continued)

Level 5 Unit 11 Pronouns   *(Use with pupil book pages 358–359.)*
Skill: Students will use *we* and *us* correctly with nouns.

LANGUAGE AND USAGE

7 | Using *we* and *us* with Nouns *(continued from page 135)*

B. Writing Application: Sentences

Imagine that you and your classmates want to raise money to buy new sports equipment for your team. Write five sentences, telling what you and the other students will do to earn that money. In each sentence, use the pronoun *we* or *us* with a noun.

Students to respond on separate paper. Answers will vary.

★ Enrichment ★

You and a group of your friends have decided to start your own companies. To attract customers, you will distribute fliers to your friends and neighbors. Describe your qualifications and the services you will provide. Write three sentences for each flier below. Use *we* or *us* with a noun in each sentence.

Answers will vary.

1. 🦴 DOG SITTING BY CARRIE AND HARRY 🦴
    _____
    _____
    _____

2. WASH WAX $10   Andy and Randy's Car Wash   WASH $2
    _____
    _____
    _____

3. CUTTER'S LANDSCAPING SERVICE
    _____
    _____
    _____

Level 5 Unit 11 Pronouns   *(Use with pupil book pages 358–359.)*
Skill: Students will use *we* and *us* correctly with nouns.

Name _____

COMPOSITION SKILL: RESEARCH REPORT

Finding Facts

A **dictionary** gives the spellings, pronunciations, and meanings of words.
An **encyclopedia** gives basic information about many subjects.
An **almanac** contains articles, lists, tables, and recent information.
An **atlas** contains maps and tables that give information about places.
Newspapers and **magazines** contain the most up-to-date information.
Nonfiction books give facts about real people, places, and events.

Write *dictionary, encyclopedia, almanac, atlas, newspaper, magazine,* or *nonfiction book* to tell where you would look for the answer to each question.
Sample answers:

1. What is the definition of the word *anthem*? **dictionary**

2. What is the title of the United States national anthem? **almanac**

3. Who wrote the music for the United States national anthem? **encyclopedia**

4. What is the pronunciation of the word *anthem*? **dictionary**

5. Who fought in the War of 1812? **encyclopedia**

6. Where is Chesapeake Bay? **atlas**

7. What happened in 1814 at Fort McHenry? **encyclopedia**

8. How many stars did the United States flag have when the national anthem was written? **encyclopedia**

9. How many verses does the United States national anthem contain? **almanac**

10. Who was John Stafford Smith? **encyclopedia**

11. Who sang the anthem at yesterday's baseball game? **newspaper**

12. When was the United States national anthem adopted by Congress? **almanac**

13. What is the world's oldest national anthem? **encyclopedia**

14. How does a songwriter go about writing the words for a song? **nonfiction book**

15. What is the national anthem of Great Britain? **encyclopedia**

Name _____

COMPOSITION SKILL: RESEARCH REPORT

Taking Notes

Take notes to help you remember what you have read. Write down **key words** that will help you recall information. Include all important facts and use your own words.

Read the paragraph below. Then write notes to answer the question that follows.

Native North Americans had many ways of scaring crows away from their cornfields. Members of some tribes kept watch from platforms overlooking the cornfields. When a crow appeared, the people waved their arms and shouted until the bird flew off. Some Creek families lived close to their fields so that they could watch for crows and scare them away. Zuñi children made unusual scarecrows to place in their fields. The Zuñis also strung ropes throughout their cornfields. From the ropes, they hung bones and rags, which would blow in the wind. The sound and the sight of these items kept most birds away. The Navajos made scarecrows for their fields too. Sometimes they hung a dead crow from a stick, hoping that it would frighten other crows.

How did native North American farmers scare crows away from their cornfields? **Sample answers:**

—tribe members kept watch from platforms

—when crows came, people waved and shouted

—Creeks lived near fields to keep watch

—Zuñi children made scarecrows

—Zuñis strung ropes and from them hung bones and rags

—Navajos made scarecrows and hung dead crows

COMPOSITION SKILL: RESEARCH REPORT

Making an Outline

Make an outline from your notes by writing the questions as the **main topics**. Place each main topic after a Roman numeral and a period. List supporting facts as **subtopics**. Place each subtopic after a capital letter and a period. The first word of a main topic or subtopic starts with a capital letter. Give your outline a title.

Use the notes below to write an outline. Rewrite the questions as main topics and the answers as subtopics. Put the subtopics in an order that makes sense. Give your outline a title.

A. **What does a gray fox look like?**
—weighs seven to thirteen pounds
—salt-and-pepper coat with rust-colored legs
—tail about fourteen inches long
—head and body about twenty-five inches long
—bushy tail with black tip **Sample answers:**

Title: The Gray Fox

I. Appearance

   A. Weighs seven to thirteen pounds

   B. Head and body about twenty-five inches long

   C. Salt-and-pepper coat with rust-colored legs

   D. Tail about fourteen inches long

   E. Bushy tail with black tip

B. **What are the gray fox's habits?**
—hunts at night
—can climb trees to escape enemies
—lives in hollow logs, caves, or among rocks **Sample answers:**

II. Habits

   A. Lives in hollow logs, caves, or among rocks

   B. Hunts at night

   C. Can climb trees to escape enemies

COMPOSITION SKILL: RESEARCH REPORT

Writing a Paragraph from an Outline

Each section of an outline is about one main idea. When you write a paragraph from an outline section, think about the main idea to write a topic sentence for the paragraph. Write the subtopics as supporting details in complete sentences.

A. Write two good topic sentences for the outline section below. Place a check beside the topic sentence you prefer.

      Great American Inventors

  I. Henry Ford (1863–1947)
    A. World-famous automobile maker
    B. Made first car in a shed behind home—1896
    C. Began the Ford Motor Company—1903
    D. Developed method of mass production
    E. Produced first inexpensive car—Model T

Sample answers:
Topic Sentence: Henry Ford, born in 1863, was one of the world's great inventors.

Topic Sentence: Henry Ford is famous all over the world as a dedicated automobile maker.

B. Now write a paragraph from the outline section above. Use the topic sentence you chose. Write supporting sentences based on the subtopics. Try to make your sentences interesting. **Sample answer:**

    Henry Ford is famous all over the world as a dedicated automobile maker. Born in 1863, Ford created his first car in 1896 in a shed behind his home. Seven years later, he began the Ford Motor Company. This inventor is remembered for mass-producing automobiles. He mass-produced the first inexpensive car and called it the Model T. If it weren't for Henry Ford, perhaps only the richest Americans would own automobiles today. Henry Ford died in 1947 after a life of many successes.

Page 141

Name _____

Writing Openings and Closings

> Begin a report with an **introduction** that captures your reader's interest and tells what the report is about. End a report with a **conclusion** that sums up the main ideas.

A. Below are two possible openings and closings for a research report about the Loch Ness monster. Put a check beside the better opening and closing.

Openings:

✓   I don't think there is a Loch Ness monster.

___   Beneath the calm surface of a lovely Scottish lake, a mysterious creature may be lurking.

Closings:

___   Maybe I will try to catch Nessie someday!

✓   Thus, the mystery of the Loch Ness monster still remains to be solved.

B. Imagine that you wrote a report on icebergs from the following outline sections. Write two good openings and two good closings for the report. Then put a check beside the opening and closing you think are better.

Icebergs

  I.   Description of iceberg
    A.   Mountain of ice floating in ocean
    B.   Piece broken off glacier (huge field of ice)
    C.   In summer, floats south from Arctic to Canada
  II.   Size of iceberg
    A.   Most of iceberg under water
    B.   May be 400 feet above water
    C.   Can be many miles long

Sample answers:

Opening: Not all mountains are made of rock. An iceberg, for example, is a towering mountain of ice.

Opening: Imagine a huge mountain made entirely of ice and floating in the ocean. That is an iceberg.

Closing: As you can see, icebergs are extremely large.

Closing: When you next hear the expression "It was only the tip of the iceberg," you'll appreciate what it means.

Page 142

Name _____

Step 4: Revise

                                   yes

Have I

replaced the weak opening with an interesting one? ☐

written a topic sentence for the paragraph? ☐

combined facts to make a sentence more interesting and moved one fact so that the order makes sense? ☐

replaced unclear pronouns and added details to make a sentence clearer? ☐

Revise the following paragraph from a research report. Use the check list above to help you. Check off each box when you have finished your revision.
- Use the space above each line, on the sides, and below the paragraph for your changes.
- Use the outline section below to write a topic sentence and to check that all the facts have been used in the paragraph.

Sample answers:

    I.   Methods of voting
      A.   All must register
      B.   All voting secret
      C.   Paper ballots dropped into locked box
      D.   Voting machines—voter moves pointer to cast vote
      E.   Some machines computerized
      F.   Absentee ballots for voters who are ill or out of town

Voting in the United States of America is an important privilege. There are several methods of voting.

This report is about voting. They must be registered. One method is to mark a paper ballot and drop it into a locked box. All voting is secret. Another method is to use a voting machine. They move pointers on the machines to cast their votes. Some of the machines who are ill or out of town are computerized. Voters can use absentee ballots.

(annotations: "However, all voters" / "and"; "voting"; "Voters")

1 Adverbs

How: The artist painted **carefully**.

When: **Soon** she displayed her work.

Where: Her paintings hung **there**.

A. Underline the adverb in each sentence. Then write whether the adverb tells *how, when,* or *where.*

1. Anna Mary Robertson always helped her mother. _____ when

2. She patiently took care of the younger children. _____ how

3. Then she became a housekeeper. _____ when

4. Her employers lived nearby. _____ where

5. A hired man worked there with her. _____ where

B. Write the adverb in each sentence. Then draw an arrow from the adverb in the sentence to the verb that it describes.

6. Eventually Anna Mary married the man, Thomas Moses. _____ Eventually

7. Anna and Tom worked hard. _____ hard

8. They successfully ran a dairy business. _____ successfully

9. Later Anna began painting. _____ Later

10. The eighty-year-old artist worked inside. _____ inside

11. Her bedroom studio was upstairs. _____ upstairs

12. Anna remembered her childhood vividly. _____ vividly

13. She skillfully used a primitive style of painting. _____ skillfully

14. Her paintings sold well. _____ well

15. Soon critics referred to her as Grandma Moses. _____ Soon

16. Exhibitors displayed her paintings everywhere. _____ everywhere

(continued)

Step 5: Proofread

Proofreading Marks

⌐	Indent.
∧	Add something.
℘	Take out something.
≡	Capitalize.
/	Make a small letter.

Proofread the following report. There are three spelling errors, four capitalization errors, and one mistake in paragraph format. There are two punctuation errors and two run-on sentences. There are three mistakes in the use of pronouns. Use proofreading marks to correct the errors. Use a dictionary to check your spelling.

the Porcupine

⌐ Have you ever met a porcupine? I have. These prickly animals are dark brown, and they have long, stiff quills on their backs, sides, and tails. Most people think that porcupines shoot their quills, this, however, is not true. the quills just have a way of coming out easily when the animal is attacked. The quills can cause serious problems for animals who are stuck by them.

Only one kind of porcupine lives in north America. They can be found mainly in pine Forests. It eats tree bark and plants, it may kill a tree by taking off the bark in this way. In the spring, the female porcupine gives birth to a single baby. Surprisingly enough, the babies have quills when they are born.

T71

Name _____

LANGUAGE AND USAGE

2 | Comparing with Adverbs

Adverb	Comparing Two	Comparing Three or More
close	closer	closest
early	earlier	earliest
swiftly	more swiftly	most swiftly

A. Write the correct form of the adverb in parentheses to complete each sentence.

1. Tala lives **closer** to school than Ali does. (close)

2. She arrived at the auditorium **earlier** than Ali did. (early)

3. Ali arrived **latest** of all the students. (late)

4. The final speaker spoke **longer** than the others. (long)

5. She talked **more excitedly** than the first speaker. (excitedly)

6. She spoke **most earnestly** of all about monkeys and apes. (earnestly)

7. Chimpanzees resemble gorillas **most closely** of all the apes. (closely)

8. Do gorillas scream **louder** than other apes do? (loud)

9. Chimpanzees learn **most quickly** of all the apes. (quickly)

10. A gibbon moves **faster** than a monkey does. (fast)

11. The gibbon can climb **higher** than a gorilla can. (high)

12. Spider monkeys climb **most gracefully** of all the monkeys. (gracefully)

13. Gibbons move **more clumsily** on land than in the trees. (clumsily)

14. Of all these apes, chimpanzees behave **most peacefully**. (peacefully)

15. A baboon fights **more often** than a gorilla does. (often)

16. Gorillas try **hardest** of all apes to avoid fights. (hard)

17. Rhesus monkeys act **most fiercely** of all monkeys. (fiercely)

18. Of all the apes, chimps act **friendliest** to humans. (friendly)

(continued)

Level 5 Unit 13 Adverbs and Prepositions *(Use with pupil book pages 414–415.)*
Skill: Students will write the comparative and the superlative forms of adverbs.

Name _____

LANGUAGE AND USAGE

1 | Adverbs *(continued from page 145)*

C. Writing Application: A Paragraph

Think of something that you do well. Your special talent could be in art, in sports, in science, or in some other field. Write a paragraph about your special talent. Use adverbs that tell how, when, and where. **Students to respond on separate paper. Answers will vary.**

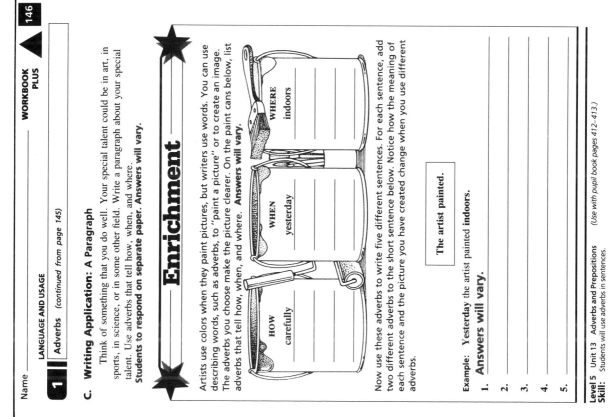

★ Enrichment ★

Artists use colors when they paint pictures, but writers use words. You can use describing words, such as adverbs, to "paint a picture" or to create an image. The adverbs you choose make the picture clearer. On the paint cans below, list adverbs that tell how, when, and where. **Answers will vary.**

HOW	WHEN	WHERE
carefully	yesterday	indoors

The artist painted.

Now use these adverbs to write five different sentences. For each sentence, add two different adverbs to the short sentence below. Notice how the meaning of each sentence and the picture you have created change when you use different adverbs.

Example: **Yesterday** the artist painted **indoors**.

1. **Answers will vary.** _____
2. _____
3. _____
4. _____
5. _____

Level 5 Unit 13 Adverbs and Prepositions *(Use with pupil book pages 412–413.)*
Skill: Students will use adverbs in sentences.

LANGUAGE AND USAGE

3 | Adjective or Adverb?

Adjectives	Adverbs
Jeanette Rankin was **confident**.	She spoke **confidently**.
She felt **well**.	She expressed herself **well**.
She did a **good** job.	She did her job **well**.

A. Underline the correct word in parentheses to complete each sentence. Then write *adjective* or *adverb* for each underlined word.

1. April 6, 1917, was (special, specially). — **adjective**

2. Would the important vote in Congress go (good, well)? — **adverb**

3. Most politicians supported the war (firm, firmly). — **adverb**

4. Their speeches that day were (good, well). — **adjective**

5. Jeanette Rankin thought war was (wrong, wrongly). — **adjective**

6. She believed (strong, strongly) in peace. — **adverb**

7. That morning Jeanette did not feel (good, well). — **adjective**

8. She rose to her feet (slow, slowly). — **adverb**

9. She expressed her opinion (good, well). — **adverb**

10. The first woman in Congress spoke (clear, clearly). — **adverb**

11. Her vote against the war was (definite, definitely). — **adjective**

12. The Speaker of the House was (angry, angrily). — **adjective**

13. The votes were counted (quick, quickly). — **adverb**

14. Jeanette's side lost (bad, badly). — **adverb**

15. Her decision had been (difficult, difficultly). — **adjective**

16. Jeanette (sure, surely) had offended many people. — **adverb**

17. Most people did not treat her (good, well). — **adverb**

18. Later, people remembered her courage (good, well). — **adverb**

(continued)

LANGUAGE AND USAGE

2 | Comparing with Adverbs (continued from page 147)

B. Writing Application: Comparison and Contrast

Pretend that you are a zoo keeper. Write a comparison of some of the animals in your zoo. Compare and contrast the habits and personalities of at least three of the animals. Include an adverb that compares in each sentence.
Students to respond on separate paper. Answers will vary.

★ Enrichment ★

Read the chart to discover some interesting facts about certain kinds of animals. Then write adverbs that compare to complete the sentences below.

ANIMALS THAT JUMP HIGH	thoroughbred horse	8 feet
	hare	7 feet
	cat	6 feet
ANIMALS THAT HAVE A LONG LIFE SPAN	Madagascar tortoise	200 years
	Asian elephant	69 years
	Pearl mussel	100 years
ANIMALS THAT RUN FAST	cheetah	71 mph
	giraffe	31 mph
	camel	10 mph
ANIMALS THAT MOVE SLOWLY	garden snail	17 feet per hour
	sloth	5 feet per hour
	red slug	6 feet per hour

puma	23 feet
impala	10 feet
tiger	13 feet
chimpanzee	51 years
raven	69 years
lobster	50 years
zebra	40 mph
lion	50 mph
hare	45 mph

Sample answers:

1. Of all the animals, the cheetah runs ____**fastest**____.

2. Of all the animals, the sloth moves ____**most slowly**____.

3. The hare can jump ____**higher**____ than the cat.

4. Of all the animals, the Madagascar tortoise lives ____**longest**____.

5. The zebra moves ____**more slowly**____ than the hare.

6. Of all the animals, the puma can jump ____**highest**____.

7. The Asian elephant lives ____**longer**____ than the chimpanzee.

8. The red slug moves ____**faster**____ than the sloth.

Now use the information in the chart to write two sentences of your own. Compare the actions of two or more animals in each sentence.

9. ____**Answers will vary.**____

10. _____

T73

Name _____

LANGUAGE AND USAGE

4 ▌ Negatives

Incorrect:	I **haven't never** used a computer.
Correct:	I **have never** used a computer.
	I **haven't ever** used a computer.

A. Rewrite each sentence, correcting the double negative.   Sample answers:

1. I never used nothing so difficult.
   I never used anything so difficult.

2. Doesn't nobody know how to work this computer?
   Doesn't anybody know how to work this computer?

3. I don't see no directions anywhere.
   I don't see any directions anywhere.

4. Won't nobody help me?
   Won't anybody help me?

5. I still don't see nothing on the screen.
   I still don't see anything on the screen.

6. No one never plugged in the computer.
   No one ever plugged in the computer.

7. I don't see the plug nowhere.
   I don't see the plug anywhere.

8. Don't none of these computer disks work?
   Don't any of these computer disks work?

9. Isn't there no one we can call for help?
   Isn't there anyone we can call for help?

10. Won't this computer never work?
    Won't this computer ever work?

Level 5 Unit 13 Adverbs and Prepositions   (Use with pupil book pages 418–419.)
Skill: Students will correct double negatives.

(continued)

Name _____

LANGUAGE AND USAGE

3 ▌ Adjective or Adverb?   (continued from page 149)

B. Writing Application: A Biography

Write a short biography of a famous person or of someone you know who per-formed a courageous act or took an unpopular stand. Use three adjectives and three adverbs in your biography. Include *good* and *well*. Underline each adjective. Circle each adverb.
Students to respond on separate paper. Answers will vary.

Enrichment

The last names of some courageous people are hidden in the sentences below. Circle each last name, and write the full name on the line. Then complete each pair of sentences. Write an adjective to complete the first sentence. Then com-plete the second sentence with an adverb that is made by adding -ly to the adjective.

Example: Rosa was tired from walking all the way from the (park,) so she sat in the first seat she could find on the bus. **Rosa Parks**

Sample answers:

Rosa was ___courageous___ . She worked ___courageously___ for civil rights.

1. Paul warned the minutemen and (forever) enjoyed the respect of the colonists.
   Paul Revere

   The night was ___clear___ . He shouted ___clearly___ .

2. Florence strode out at (night in gales) and rain to help the wounded soldiers.
   Florence Nightingale

   Her lamp was ___bright___ . It shone ___brightly___ in the night.

3. As Harriet waited for the signal, the slave was forced to hide behind the (bathtub many) hours. **Harriet Tubman**

   Harriet was ___brave___ . She fought ___bravely___ for freedom.

4. Neil held in his (arm strong) evidence that the United States was the first to land a person on the moon. **Neil Armstrong**

   Neil was ___confident___ . He stood ___confidently___ on the lunar surface.

Level 5 Unit 13 Adverbs and Prepositions   (Use with pupil book pages 416–417.)
Skill: Students will use adjectives and adverbs correctly.

Page 153

5 ‖ Prepositions

The architect displayed the drawing **of** the house.
    preposition   object

She showed it **to** them.
    preposition object

A. Underline the preposition in each sentence. Then write the object of the preposition.

1. Harriet designs buildings of many types.	types
2. She is working on several projects.	projects
3. Her office is inside this building.	building
4. Blueprints are scattered across her desk.	desk
5. Her drafting table is under a skylight.	skylight
6. A detailed model is by the window.	window
7. Several miniature trees are around it.	it
8. Harriet spends long hours in this office.	office
9. However, she also goes to the construction site.	site
10. She brings the blueprints with her.	her
11. A supervisor meets her at the gate.	gate
12. Harriet walks through the structure.	structure
13. She checks below the ground level.	level
14. She climbs up the ladder.	ladder
15. The workers talk about the project.	project
16. Problems are discussed during this meeting.	meeting
17. These problems cannot wait until the last minute.	minute
18. The architect must find solutions for them.	them

(continued)

Page 152

4 ‖ Negatives (continued from page 151)

B. Writing Application: An Advertisement

Pretend that you work for an advertising company. You must write an advertisement for a new computer. Use a negative in each sentence of your advertisement.
Be sure that you do not use any double negatives.
Students to respond on separate paper. Answers will vary.

Enrichment

Computer information is usually stored on small, flat disks. These disks are very sensitive and require special handling. The warning signs below show the things we should not do when we are working with computer disks. Write a sentence for each warning sign. Use one negative word in each sentence.
Sample answers:

1.

Never scratch a disk. _____

3.

Place nothing that can
spill next to a disk. _____

2. _____

Don't bend a disk. _____

4. _____

Don't ever leave disks in
direct sunlight. _____

Name _____

LANGUAGE AND USAGE

6 | Prepositional Phrases

preposition   object   object
Mistakes **in construction** and **manufacturing** can be dangerous.
              prepositional phrase

                   preposition   object
Laws protect people **from these mistakes.**
                         prepositional phrase

A. Write the prepositional phrase in each sentence. Underline the preposition once and the object of the preposition twice.

1. The Tacoma Narrows Bridge in Washington opened forty-five years ago.
   in Washington

2. The bridge was built across Puget Sound.   **across Puget Sound**

3. At that time, it was the world's third largest suspension bridge.
   At that time

4. Soon passengers inside cars and buses noticed that the bridge swayed.
   inside cars and buses

5. After a few weeks, people began calling the bridge Galloping Gertie.
   After a few weeks

6. Crossing the bridge resembled a ride on a roller coaster or a boat.
   on a roller coaster or a boat

7. During strong winds, the bridge swayed violently.
   During strong winds

8. Officials finally closed the bridge to vehicles and people.
   to vehicles and people

9. Eventually the deck fell into the water.   **into the water**

10. Now models of bridges must first be tested.
    of bridges

(continued)

Level 5   Unit 13   Adverbs and Prepositions   (Use with pupil book pages 422–423.)
Skill: Students will identify prepositional phrases, prepositions, and the objects of prepositions.

Name _____

LANGUAGE AND USAGE

5 | Prepositions   (continued from page 153)

B. Writing Application: A Persuasive Letter

A new community center is being planned for your town. As an architect, you would like to design the building. Write a persuasive letter to the building committee, telling why you think your design is best. Include at least five prepositions in your letter. Underline the prepositions.
Students to respond on separate paper. Answers will vary.

★ Enrichment ★

Below is an architect's plan for a new house. The new owners, Mr. and Mrs. Lang, want to see where their furniture will fit. You can help them with the arrangement by drawing the furniture where you think it should be placed. Use the symbols shown below for the furniture.

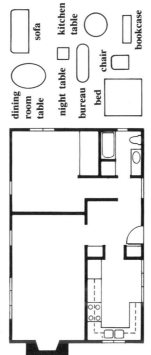

dining room table
sofa
night table
kitchen table
bureau
bed
chair
bookcase

Now write a paragraph, describing your suggestions for the placement of the furniture. Use a preposition in each sentence. Underline each preposition once and the object of the preposition twice.
Answers will vary.

_____
_____
_____
_____
_____

Level 5   Unit 13   Adverbs and Prepositions   (Use with pupil book pages 420–421.)
Skill: Students will use prepositions in sentences.

LANGUAGE AND USAGE

7 | Object Pronouns in Prepositional Phrases

> The exercise teacher ran past **me**.
> I jogged after the other **students** and **him**.

A. Rewrite each sentence, using the correct pronoun in parentheses. Then underline the prepositional phrase in the sentence that you wrote.

1. Exercise classes are held near (us, we).
   Exercise classes are held near us.

2. Ms. Jay and Mr. Petrie usually arrive before my parents and (I, me).
   Ms. Jay and Mr. Petrie usually arrive before my parents and me.

3. From (her, she) and (him, he), we learn different exercises.
   From her and him, we learn different exercises.

4. We always do warm-up exercises with the other students and (them, they).
   We always do warm-up exercises with the other students and them.

5. Ms. Jay explains the exercises to (we, us).
   Ms. Jay explains the exercises to us.

6. No one except Mom and (I, me) can do sit-ups.
   No one except Mom and me can do sit-ups.

7. The student beside Dad and (her, she) couldn't do pushups.
   The student beside Dad and her couldn't do pushups.

8. One beginner behind Mom and (he, him) thinks that leg lifts are easy.
   One beginner behind Mom and him thinks that leg lifts are easy.

9. For my parents and (I, me), these exercise classes are fun.
   For my parents and me, these exercise classes are fun.

10. Without (they, them) we wouldn't stay fit.
    Without them we wouldn't stay fit.

(continued)

Level 5 Unit 13 Adverbs and Prepositions   *(Use with pupil book pages 424–425.)*
Skill: Students will use object pronouns in prepositional phrases and will identify prepositional phrases.

LANGUAGE AND USAGE

6 | Prepositional Phrases *(continued from page 155)*

B. Writing Application: A Description

Think of an exciting or unusual trip that you have taken. Write a paragraph, describing that trip. Use at least five prepositional phrases in your description. Underline each prepositional phrase.
Students to respond on separate paper. Answers will vary.

★ Enrichment

Below is a map of the town of Shambletown, which is in the state of Disrepair. Buster is anxious to get to the Fix-It Shop. Draw the route he should follow. He may not cross any broken bridges.

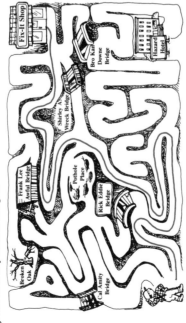

Now write directions, telling Buster how to reach the Fix-It Shop. Use a prepositional phrase in each sentence of your directions.
Answers will vary.

Level 5 Unit 13 Adverbs and Prepositions   *(Use with pupil book pages 422–423.)*
Skill: Students will use prepositional phrases in sentences.

Name _____ WORKBOOK PLUS 159

LANGUAGE AND USAGE

8 | Adverb or Preposition?

Adverb: The drawbridge moved **down**.
Preposition: The knight rode **down** the path.

A. If the sentence has an adverb, write the adverb. If it has a prepositional phrase, underline the prepositional phrase and write the preposition.

1. Several tourists mingled outside. — outside
2. More visitors waited inside. — inside
3. Hilary walked up the stairs. — up
4. A knight in armor guarded the entrance. — in
5. He put his helmet down. — down
6. She passed by. — by
7. She peered inside the darkened room. — inside
8. A guide invited her in. — in
9. Hilary strolled around. — around
10. Armor was displayed along all the walls. — along
11. Hilary read the explanation above the armor. — above
12. She looked up. — up
13. Decorated shields dangled above. — above
14. Heavy metal helmets hung below the shields. — below
15. Hilary looked down a long hallway. — down
16. Near the end was a jewel display. — Near
17. Hilary walked by the display. — by
18. Shields had glittering jewels around their edges. — around

(continued)

Level 5   Unit 13   Adverbs and Prepositions   (Use with pupil book pages 426—427.)
Skill: Students will identify and will distinguish between adverbs and prepositions.

Name _____ WORKBOOK PLUS 158

LANGUAGE AND USAGE

7 | Object Pronouns in Prepositional Phrases (continued from page 157)

B. Writing Application: A List

Think of an activity that you and other students do in gym class. Write a list of sentences, explaining the steps involved in this activity. In each sentence, use a prepositional phrase with an object pronoun. Underline the prepositional phrases. **Students to respond on separate paper. Answers will vary.**

★ Enrichment ★

Read the first sentence in each pair below. Then write a prepositional phrase to complete the second sentence. The phrases you write are parts of common expressions. Each prepositional phrase should consist of a preposition and at least one pronoun.

1. Bo and Mo will learn crossovers. Just keep **after them** .
2. He just did one hundred pushups! I can't get **over it** !
3. Millicent just can't do knee bends. Stop picking **on her** .
4. Zeke and Joe are having trouble. Can we cover **for them** ?
5. Si and Sophie need our support. Let's all get **behind Si and her** .
6. Sophie doesn't know her own ability. In fact, she runs rings **around us** in weightlifting.
7. Sophie loves weightlifting. She's nuts **about it** .
8. Nella and I are learning to do leg lifts. Try to bear **with us** .
9. We know that the team can do better. Let's build a fire **under them** .
10. Mac tried to do fewer sit-ups, but he didn't get away **with it** .
11. Zoe and Mac think these classes are difficult. The classes are beginning to get **to Zoe and him** .
12. Ava and he don't listen to the instructions. The teachers find it difficult to get through **to Ava and him** .

Level 5   Unit 13   Adverbs and Prepositions   (Use with pupil book pages 424—425.)
Skill: Students will write prepositional phrases with object pronouns.

LANGUAGE AND USAGE

8 Adverb or Preposition? *(continued from page 159)*

B. Writing Application: A Speech

Pretend that you are a museum guide in the year 2525. You are taking a group of students around a display of twentieth-century machines. Write a short speech, describing where you are walking and what is on exhibit in the museum. Use at least three adverbs and three prepositions in your speech.

Students to respond on separate paper. Answers will vary.

★ Enrichment ★

Imagine that you are a tour guide at an ancient castle. Each day you answer many questions from visitors. Using the picture below, write a sentence to answer each of the following questions. Use a word from the box in each sentence. Write your sentences on another piece of paper.

| around | outside | over | up | down |
| inside | below | above | near | under |

Answers will vary.

1. How do people get into the castle?

2. Where does the moat flow?

3. How do you get to the turret?

4. Where is the gatehouse?

5. Where is the fortress?

6. Can you see the moat from the tower?

Level 5 Unit 13 Adverbs and Prepositions *(Use with pupil book pages 426–427.)*
Skill: Students will identify adverbs and prepositions in sentences.

Index

Notes

Notes

Notes

Notes